AUDELS

PLUMBERS and PIPE FITTERS
Library

Materials • Tools • Calculations

by Jules Oravetz, Sr.

Registered Professional Engineer

THEODORE AUDEL & CO.
a division of
HOWARD W. SAMS & CO., INC.
4300 West 62nd Street
Indianapolis Indiana, 46206

FIRST EDITION

SIXTH PRINTING—1974

Library of Congress Catalog Card Number: 67-17396

Foreword

Plumbing and pipe fitting plays a major role in the construction of every residential, commercial, and industrial building. Of all the building trades, none are as essential to the health and well-being of the community in general, and the building occupants in particular, as the plumbing trade. It is the obligation and responsibility of every plumber to uphold this vital trust placed in him in the installation of the plumbing materials and equipment.

Every plumbing installation is governed by certain rules and regulations set forth in local plumbing codes that have been adopted from standards established at either a local, state, or federal level. In addition, each installation is subject to inspection by a licensed inspector to insure that all rules and regulations have been complied with. All this coupled with the usual practice of requiring those persons engaged in plumbing installation to pass an examination for a license shows the great importance placed on this phase of the building trades.

This series of books have been written to aid those persons who wish to become plumbers as well as those who are already actively engaged in this occupation. This, the first of three volumes, deals with general information that is valuable to the plumber or pipe fitter. Simple mathematics and physics necessary to make the understanding of the material in the rest of the library is included. The materials and tools used in plumbing are also discussed as well as the methods of using them. Questions and answers for the usual licensing examination are also given and should be found most helpful by anyone wishing to obtain his license.

JULES ORAVETZ, SR.

About the Author . . .

Mr. Oravetz is a Registered Professional Engineer in Iowa, Kansas, Colorado, Wisconsin, and Michigan. In addition, he is a licensed Stationary Engineer. For the past 15 years he has been chief of a major engineering and maintenance division with the responsibility of a five-state area. He is also a consultant for the maintenance of building and grounds for the Recreation and Parks Department of a major midwestern city.

Contents

CHAPTER 4

Sheet-metal gauges—how sheet lead is manufactured—sheet tin—tin plate—roofing plates—sheet metal—galvanized sheet metal—sheet brass—bronze—sheet copper—temper—summary—review questions

CHAPTER 5

Wrought-iron or steel welded pipe—threaded pipe joints—weight of pipe—manufacture and tests—bursting and safe working pressures—cast-iron pipe—copper pipe—brass pipe—lead pipe—tubes—plastic piping—summary—review questions

CHAPTER 6

Straightedges—squares—levels—plumb bobs—chalk lines—marking or scratch awls—dividers and trammels—punches—T-handle tap wrenches—measuring tapes—vises—files and rasps—saws—scrapers—chisels—augers—twist drills—power tools—power rodding equipment—pipe-threading dies—pipe stock—pipe vise—pipe-threading machines—pipe tap—pipe cutters—pipe reamers—pipe-bending tools—tube cutters and reamers—flaring tools—hammers—screwdrivers—wrenches—soldering tools — summary — review questions

CHAPTER 7

Solder—miscellaneous solders—soldering fluxes—soldering bolts or bits—soft soldering—soldering with a torch—sweating—lead burning—soldering copper tubing and piping—hard-solder joints for copper tubing—cutting copper tube—solder-joint valves—summary—review questions

CHAPTER 8

Judging the solder—proportioning the solder—cleaning solder—preparing joint for wiping—length of joint—wiping the joint—wiping a branch joint—bending lead pipe—summary—review questions

CHAPTER 9

CHAPTER 10

CHAPTER 1

Mathematics

Plumbing and heating are important factors in construction, and vital to the health, morale, and welfare of building occupants. Piping is the basic factor in plumbing, and can be compared to the veins and arteries of the human body. Generally, the piping is invisible, but working for the well being and comfort of those in the building. Plumbing pipe is classified as supply and waste, with the supply piping providing pure water to fixtures and waste piping removing that liquid which can not be classified as pure water.

Design is important in planning piping systems. Piping must be durable, have leakproof joints, be of proper size for the intended purpose, and in accordance with codes which are set up in almost all localities for purposes of protecting the health and welfare of the individual and public. In order to plan and compute well, a knowledge of mathematics is of great importance to the plumber and steam fitter. Therefore, a general review of mathematics with some reference tables is presented.

SYMBOLS

The various processes in mathematics are usually indicated by symbols for convenience and brevity. The following are the numerous symbols commonly used.

$=$ means equal to, or equality;

$-$ means minus, less, or subtraction;

$+$ means plus, or addition;

$\times$ means multiplied by, or multiplication;

$\div$ or /   means divided by, or division;

^{2} are indexes or powers, meaning that the number
^{3} to which they are added is to be squared or cubed;
thus, 2^2 means 2 squared; 2^3 means 2 cubed;

:   is to⎫
:: so is ⎬ are signs of proportion;
:   to   ⎭

$\sqrt{}$ is the radical sign and means that the square root of the number before which it is placed is to be extracted;

$\sqrt[3]{}$ means that the cube root of the number before which it is placed is to be extracted;

— the bar indicates that all of the numbers under it are to be taken together;

( ) the parentheses means that all of the numbers between are to be taken as one quantity;

.   the decimal point means decimal parts; thus, 2.5 means 2-5/10, 0.46 means 46/100;

°   means degrees;

::: means hence;

π means ratio of the circumference of a circle to its diameter; numerically 3.1416;

″   means inches, seconds, or second;

′   means feet, minutes, or prime.

ABBREVIATIONS

In addition to the symbols just given, certain abbreviations and definitions are used. The practice of writing *"pounds per square inch"* instead of *"lbs. per sq. in."* is not preferred, because in reading it, the eye has to travel faster, resulting in fatigue and less speed in reading. The same thing is true of the excessive use of capital letters. It is a psychological fact that the omission of these capital letters results in less fatigue to the reader, though he may not be conscious of the fact.

The following abbreviations are commonly used:

A or a = area
A.W.G. = American wire gauge
bbl. = barrels
B or b = breadth
bhp = brake horse power
B.M. = board measure
Btu = British thermal units
B.W.G = Birmingham wire gauge
B & S = Brown and Sharpe wire gauge (American wire gauge)
C of g = center of gravity
cond. = condensing
cu. = cubic
cyl. = cylinder
D or d = depth or diameter
deg. = degrees
diam. = diameter
evap. = evaporation
F = coefficient of friction; Fahrenheit
F or f = force or factor of safety
ft. lbs. = foot pounds
gals. = gallons
H or h = height, or head of water
HP = horsepower
IHP = indicated horsepower
L or 1 = length
lbs. = pounds
lbs. per sq. in. = pounds per square inch
o.d. = outside diameter (pipes)
oz. = ounces
pt. = pint
P or p = pressure or load
psi = pounds per square inch
R or r = radius
rpm = revolutions per minute
□ ′ = square feet
sq. ft. = square foot
sq. in. = square inch
□ ″ = square inches

sq. yd. = square yard
T or t = thickness, or temperature
temp. = temperature
V or v = velocity
vol. = volume
W or w = weight
W.I. = wrought iron

DEFINITIONS

Abstract Number—One which does not refer to any particular object.

Acute Triangle—One which has three acute angles.

Altitude (of a parallelogram or trapezoid)—the perpendicular distance between its parallel sides.

Altitude (of a prism)—The perpendicular distance between its bases.

Altitude (of a pyramid or cone)—The perpendicular distance from its vertex to the plane of its base.

Altitude (of a triangle)—A line drawn perpendicular to the base from the angle opposite.

Analysis—The process of investigating principles and solving problems independently of set rules.

Angle—The difference in direction of two lines proceeding from the same point called the vertex.

Area—The surface included within the lines which bound a plane figure.

Arithmetic—The science of numbers and the art of computation.

Base (of a triangle)—The side on which it may be supposed to stand.

Board Measure—A unit for measuring lumber being a volume of a board 12-in. wide, 1-ft. long, and 1-in. thick.

Circle—A plane figure bounded by a curved line, called the circumference, every point of which is equally distant from a point within, called the center.

Complex Fraction—One whose numerator or denominator is a fraction.

Compound Fraction—A fraction of a fraction.

Composite Numbers—A number which can be divided by other integers besides itself and one.

Compound Numbers—Units of two or more denominations of the same kind.

Concrete Number—A number used to designate objects or quantities.

Cone—A body having a circular base, and whose convex surface tapers uniformly to the vertex.

Cube—A parallelopipedon whose faces are all equal squares.

Cubic Measure—A measure of volume involving three dimensions —length, breadth, and thickness.

Cylinder—A body bounded by a uniformly curved surface, its ends being equal and parallel circles.

Decimal Scale—One in which the order of progression is uniformly ten.

Demonstration—Process of reasoning by which a truth or principle is established.

Denomination—Name of the unit of a concrete number.

Diagonal (of a plane figure)—A straight line joining the vertices of two angles not adjacent.

Diameter (of a circle)—A line passing through its center and terminated at both ends by the circumference.

Diameter (of a sphere)—A straight line passing through the center of the sphere, and terminated at both ends by its surface.

Equilateral Triangle—One which has all its sides equal.

Even Number—A number that can be exactly divided by two.

Exact Divisor of a Number—A whole number that will divide that number without a remainder.

Factors—One of two or more quantities which, when multiplied together, produces a given quantity.

Factors of a Number—Numbers which, when multiplied together, make that number.

Fraction—A number which expresses equal parts of a whole thing or quantity.

Frustum (of a pyramid or cone)—The part which remains after cutting off the top by a plane parallel to the base.

Geometry—That branch of pure mathematics that treats of space and its relations.

Greatest Common Divisor—The greatest number that will exactly divide two or more numbers.

Hypotenuse (of a right triangle)—The side opposite the right angle.

Improper Fraction—One whose numerator equals or exceeds its denominator.

Integer—A number that represents whole things.

Involution—The multiplication of a quantity by itself any number of times; raising a number to a given power.

Isosceles Triangle—One which has two of its sides equal.

Least Common Multiple—Least number that is exactly divisible by two or more numbers.

Like Numbers—Same kind of unit, expressing the same kind of quantity.

Mathematics—The science of quantity.

Measure—That by which the extent, quantity, capacity, volume, or dimensions in general is ascertained by some fixed standard.

Mensuration—The process of measuring.

Multiple of a Number—Any number exactly divisible by that number.

Number—A unit or collection of units.

Obtuse Triangle—One which has one obtuse angle.

Odd Number—A number which cannot be divided by two.

Parallelogram—Quadrilateral which has its opposite sides parellel.

Parallelopipedon—A prism bounded by six parallelograms, the opposite ones being parallel and equal.

Percentage—Rate per hundred.

Perpendicular (of a right triangle)—The side which forms a right angle with the base.

Perimeter (of a polygon)—The sum of its sides.

Plane Figure—A plane surface.

Polygon—A plane figure bounded by straight lines.

Power—Product arising from multiplying a number.

Prime Factor—A prime number used as a factor.

Prime Number—A number exactly divisible by some number other than one or itself.

Prism—A solid whose ends are equal and parallel polygons, and whose sides are parallelograms.

Problem—A question requiring an operation.

Proper Fraction—One whose numerator is less than its denominator.

Pyramid—A body having for its base a polygon, and for its other sides or facets three or more triangles which terminate in a common point called the vertex.

Quadrilateral—A plane figure bounded by four straight lines and having four angles.

15

Quantity—That which can be increased, diminished, or measured.

Radius (of a circle)—A line extending from its center to any point on the circumference. It is one-half the diameter.

Radius (of a sphere)—A straight line drawn from the center to any point on the surface.

Rectangle—A parallelogram with all its angles right angles.

Rhombus—A parallelogram whose sides are all equal, but whose angles are not right angles.

Rhomboid—A parallelogram whose opposite sides only are equal, but whose angles are not right angles.

Right Triangle—One which has a right angle.

Root—A factor repeated to produce a power.

Rule—A prescribed method of performing an operation.

Scale—Order of progression on which any system of notation is founded.

Scalene Triangle—One which has all of its sides unequal.

Simple Fraction—One whose numerator and denominator are whole numbers.

Simple Number—Either an abstract number or a concrete number of but one denomination.

Slant Height (of a cone)—A straight line from the vertex to the circumference of the base.

Slant Height (of a pyramid)—The perpendicular distance from its vertex to one of the sides of the base.

Sphere—A body bounded by a uniformly curved surface, all the points of which are equally distant from a point within called the center.

Square—A rectangle whose sides are equal.

Trapezoid—A quadrilateral, two of whose sides are parallel and two oblique.

Trapezium—A quadrilateral having no two sides parallel.

Triangle—A plane figure bounded by three sides, and having three angles.

Unit—A single thing or a definite quantity.

Unity—Unit of an abstract number.

Uniform Scale—One in which the order of progression is the same throughout the entire succession of units.

Unlike Numbers—Different kinds of units, used to express different kinds of quantity.

Varying Scale—One in which the order of progression is not the same throughout the entire succession of units.

NOTATION AND NUMERATION

By definition, *notation* in arithmetic is *the writing down of figures to express a number*. A *numeration* is *the reading of the number or collection of figures already written*.

By means of the ten figures which follow, any number can be expressed.

$$0 \ 1 \ 2 \ 3 \ 4 \ 5 \ 6 \ 7 \ 8 \ 9$$

The system in Table 1 is called *Arabic notation,* and is the system in ordinary everyday use.

Table 2 shows the *Roman* system of notation often used, especially to denote the year of construction or manufacture.

The following ten formulas include the elementary operations of arithmetic.

1. The sum = all the parts added.
2. The difference = the minuend − the subtrahend.
3. The minuend = the subtrahend + the difference.
4. The subtrahend = the minuend − the difference.
5. The product = the multiplicand × the multiplier.
6. The multiplicand = the product ÷ the multiplier.

7. The multiplier = the product ÷ the multiplicand.
8. The quotient = the dividend ÷ the divisor.
9. The dividend = the quotient × the divisor.
10. The divisor = the dividend ÷ the quotient.

Table 1. Numeration Table

Names of Units	Billions	Millions	Thousands	Units	Thousandths
Grouping of the Units	Hundred-billions Ten-billions Billions 7 8 6,	Hundred-millions Ten-millions Millions 5 4 3,	Hundred-thousands Ten-thousands Thousands 2 0 1,	Hundreds Tens Units 2 8 2,	Decimal point . Tenths Hundredths Thousandths 4 8 9

Table 2. Roman Numerals

I = 1	VIII = 8	XV = 15	XL = 40	D = 500
II = 2	IX = 9	XVI = 16	L = 50	M = 1000
III = 3	X = 10	XVII = 17	LX = 60	$\overline{X}$ = 10,000
IV = 4	XI = 11	XVIII = 18	LXX = 70	$\overline{M}$ = 1,000,000
V = 5	XII = 12	XIX = 19	LXXX = 80	
VI = 6	XIII = 13	XX = 20	XC = 90	
VII = 7	XIV = 14	XXX = 30	C = 100	

Addition

The sign of addition is + and is read *plus;* thus 7 + 3 is read *seven plus three.*

Rule A—Write the numbers to be added so that like orders of units stand in the same column.

Rule B—Commencing with the lowest order, or at the right hand, add each column separately, and if the sum can be expressed by one figure, write it under the column added.

Rule C—If the sum of any column contains more than one figure, write the unit figure under the column added, and add the remaining figure or figures to the next column.

Examples:

7,060	248,124	13,579,802
9,420	4,321	93
1,743	889,966	478,652
4,004	457,902	87,547,289
22,227 Ans.		

Use great care in placing the numbers in vertical lines, as irregularity in writing them down is one cause of mistakes.

Subtraction

The sign of subtraction is − and is read *minus*; thus 10 − 7 is read *ten minus seven* or *seven from ten*.

Rule A—Write down the sum so that the units stand under the units, the tens under the tens, etc., etc.

Rule B—Begin with the units, and take the under from the upper figure and put the remainder beneath the line.

Rule C—If the lower figure is the larger, add ten to the upper figure, and then subtract and put the remainder down; this borrowed ten must be deducted from the next column of figures where it is represented by 1.

Examples:

892	2,572	9,999
46	1,586	8,971
846 remainder.		

Multiplication

The sign of multiplication is × and is read *times* or *multiplied by;* thus 6 × 8 is read 6 times 8 is 48, or 6 multiplied by 8 is 48. The principle of multiplication is the same as addition; thus 3 × 8 = 24 is the same as 8 + 8 + 8 = 24.

Rule—Place the unit figure of the multiplier under the unit figure of the multiplicand and proceed as in the following examples:

Example—Multiply 846 by 8; and 478,692 by 143. Arrange them thus:

```
        846              487,692
          8                  143
       ————              ———————
       6768              1463076
                         1950768
                          487692
                        ————————
                        69739956
```

Rule—If the multiplier has ciphers at its end, place it as in the following examples:

Example—Multiply 83567 by 50; and 898 by 2800.

```
      83567                  898
         50                 2800
    ———————              ———————
    4178350               718400
                            1796
                         ———————
                         2514400
```

Division

The sign of division is ÷ and is read *divided by,* thus 8 ÷ 2 is read *eight divided by two.* There are two methods of division known as *short division* and *long division.*

Short Division
To divide by any number up to 12.
Rule—Put the dividend down with the divisor to the left of it, with a small curved line separating it, as in the following:
Example—Divide 7,865,432 by 6.

$$6)\overline{7,865,432}$$
$$\overline{1,310,905} \text{ —2}$$

Here at the last, 6 into 32 goes 5 times and 2 over; always place the number that is left over as a fraction. This would be

2/6, the top figure being the remainder and the bottom figure the divisor. It should be put close to the quotient; thus 1,310,-905 2/6.

To divide by any number up to 12 with a cipher or ciphers after it, as 20, 70, 500, 7000, etc.

Rule—Place the sum down as in the last example, then mark off from the right of the dividend as many figures as there are ciphers in the divisor; also mark off the ciphers in the divisor; then divide the remaining figures by the number remaining in the divisor, thus:

Example—Divide 9,876,804 by 40.

$$40)\underline{9,876,804}$$
$$246,920\ 4/40$$

Long Division
To divide any number by a large divisor of two or more figures.

Example—Divide 18,149 by 56.

$$56)\ 18149(324\ 5/56$$
$$\underline{168}$$
$$\underline{134}$$
$$\underline{112}$$
$$\underline{229}$$
$$\underline{224}$$
$$5$$

In the above operation, the process is as follows: As neither 1 nor 18 will contain the divisor, take the first three figures (181) for the first partial dividend. The number 56 is contained in 181 three times, with a remainder. Write the 3 as the first figure in the quotient, and then multiply the divisor by this quotient figure thus: 3 times 56 is 168, which when subtracted from 181 leaves 13. To this remainder annex (bring down) 4, the next figure in the dividend, thus forming 134 which is the next partial dividend. The number 56 is contained in 134 two times with a remainder.

Thus, 2 times 56 is 112, which subtracted from 134 leaves 22. To the remainder bring down 9, the last figure in the dividend, forming 229, the last partial dividend. The number 56 is contained in 229 four times with a remainder. Thus: 4 times 56 is 224, which, subtracted from 229 gives 5, the final remainder; thus completing the operation of long division.

Factors

Numbers 4 and 5 are factors of 20, because 4 multiplied by 5 equals 20.

Rule—Divide the given number by any prime factor; divide the quotient in the same manner, and so continue the division until the quotient is a prime number. The several divisors and the last quotient will be the prime factors required.

Example—What are the prime factors of 798?

$$
\begin{array}{r|r}
2 & 798 \\ \hline
3 & 399 \\ \hline
7 & 133 \\ \hline
19 & 19 \\ \hline
& 1
\end{array}
$$

Greatest Common Divisor

Number 5 is the greatest common divisor of 10 and 15, because it is the greatest number that will exactly divide each of them.

Rule—Write the numbers in a line, with a vertical line at the left, and divide by any factor common to all the numbers. Divide the quotient in like manner, and continue the dividend till a set of quotients is obtained that are prime to each other. Multiply all the divisors together and the product will be the greatest common divisor sought.

Example—What is the greatest common divisor of 72, 120, and 440?

4	72	120	440
2	18	30	110
	9	15	55

Least Common Divisor

Number 6 is the least common multiple of 2 and 3, because it is the least number exactly divisible by those numbers.

Rule—Resolve the given numbers into their prime factors. Multiply together all the prime factors of the largest number, and such prime factors of the other numbers as are not found in the largest number. Their product will be the least common multiple. When a prime factor is repeated in any of the given numbers it must be taken as many times in the multiple as the greatest number of times it appears in any of the given numbers.

Example—Find the least common multiple of 60, 84, and 132.

$$60 = 2 \times 2 \times 3 \times 5$$
$$84 = 2 \times 2 \times 3 \times 7$$
$$132 = 2 \times 2 \times 3 \times 11$$
$$(2 \times 2 \times 3 \times 11) \times 5 \times 7 = 4620$$

Fractions

If a unit or whole number is divided into two equal parts, one of these parts is called *one-half,* written $1/2$.

To reduce a common fraction to its lowest terms.

Rule—Divide both terms by their greatest common divisor.

Example:

$$\frac{9}{15} = \frac{3}{5}$$

To change an improper fraction to a mixed number.

Rule—Divide the numerator by the denominator; the quotient is the whole number and the remainder placed over the denominator is the fraction.

Example:

$$\frac{23}{4} = 5\text{-}3/4$$

To change a mixed number to an improper fraction.
Rule—Multiply the whole number by the denominator of the fraction; to the product add the numerator and place the sum over the denominator.

Example:

$$1\text{-}3/8 = 11/8$$

To reduce a compound to a simple fraction, and to multiply fractions.
Rule—Multiply the numerators together for a new numerator and the denominators together for a new denominator.

Example:

$$\frac{1}{2}\text{of}\frac{2}{3} = \frac{2}{6}; \text{ also } \frac{1}{2} \times \frac{2}{3} = \frac{2}{6}$$

To reduce a complex to a simple fraction.
Rule—The numerator and denominator must each first be given the form of a simple fraction: then multiply the numerator of the upper fraction by the denominator of the lower for the new numerator, and the denominator of the upper by the numerator of the lower for the new denominator.

Example:

$$\frac{7/8}{1\text{-}3/4} = \frac{7/8}{7/4} = \frac{28}{56} = \frac{1}{2}$$

To add fractions,
Rule—Reduce them to a common denominator, add the numerators, and place their sum over the common denominator.

Example:

$$\frac{1}{2} + \frac{1}{4} = \frac{4+2}{8} = \frac{6}{8} = \frac{3}{4}$$

To subtract fractions.

Rule—Reduce them to a common denominator, subtract the numerators, and place the difference over the common denominator.

Example:

$$\frac{1}{2} - \frac{1}{4} = \frac{4-2}{8} = \frac{2}{8} = \frac{1}{4}$$

To multiply fractions.

Rule—(Multiplying by a whole number) Multiply the numerator or divide the denominator by the whole number.

Example:

$$\frac{1}{2} \times 3 = \frac{3}{2} = 1\frac{1}{2}$$

To divide fractions.

Rule—(Dividing by a whole number) Divide the numerator, or multiply the denominator by the whole number.

Example:

(dividing) $\frac{10}{13} \div 5 = \frac{2}{13}$; (multiplying) $\frac{10}{13} \div 5 = \frac{10}{65} = \frac{2}{13}$

Rule—(Dividing by a fraction) Invert the divisor and proceed as in multiplication.

Example:

$$\frac{3}{4} \div \frac{5}{7} = \frac{3}{4} \times \frac{7}{5} = \frac{21}{20} = 1\frac{1}{20}$$

DECIMAL FRACTIONS

Any decimal or combination of a decimal and integer may be read by applying Table 2.

The important thing about decimals is to *always plainly put down the decimal point*. In case of a column of figures, as in addition, care should be taken to have all the decimal points exactly under each other.

To reduce a decimal to a common fraction.

Rule—Write down the demominator and reduce the common fraction thus obtained to its lowest terms.

Example:

$$.25 = \frac{25}{100} = \frac{1}{4}$$

Table 2. Numeration of Decimals

Ten thousands	Thousands	Hundreds	Tens	Units	Decimal point	Tenths	Hundredths	Thousandths	Ten thousandths	Hundred thousandths
1	**2**	**3**	**4**	**5**	·	**1**	**2**	**3**	**4**	**5**
5th order	4th order	3rd order	2nd order	1st order		1st order	2nd order	3rd order	4th order	5th order
		Integers						Decimals		

To add and subtract decimals.

Rule—Place the numbers in a column with the decimal points under each other and proceed as in simple addition or subtraction.

Examples:

Addition	Subtraction
.5	1.25
.25	.75
1.75	.50
2.50	

To multiply decimals.

Rule—Proceed as in simple multiplication and point off as many places as there are places in the multiplier and multiplicand.

Example:

$$.1 \times .0025 = .00025$$

To divide decimals.

Rule—Proceed as in simple division, and from the right hand of the quotient, point off as many places for decimals as the decimal places in the dividend exceed those in the divisor.

Example:

$$1.5 \div .25 = 6$$

To reduce common fractions to decimals.

Rule—Divide the numerator by the denominator and carry out the division to as many decimal places as desired.

Example:

$$\frac{4}{5} = 4 \div 5 = .8$$

27

Table 3. Fractions and Decimal Equivalents

1/64 = .015625	11/32 = .34375	43/64 = .671875
1/32 = .03125	23/64 = .359375	11/16 = .6875
3/64 = .046875	3/8 = .375	45/64 = .703125
1/16 = .0625	25/64 = .390625	23/32 = .71875
5/64 = 0.78125	13/32 = .40625	47/64 = .734375
3/32 = .09375	27/64 = .421875	3/4 = .75
7/64 = .109375	7/16 = .4375	49/64 = .765625
1/8 = .125	29/64 = .453125	25/32 = .78125
9/64 = .140625	15/32 = .46875	51/64 = .796875
5/32 = .15625	31/64 = .484375	13/16 = .8125
11/64 = .171875	1/2 = .5	53/64 = .828125
3/16 = .1875	33/64 = .515625	27/32 = .84375
13/64 = .203125	17/32 = .53125	55/64 = .859375
7/32 = .21875	35/64 = .546875	7/8 = .875
15/16 = .234375	9/16 = .546875	57/64 = .890625
1/4 = .25	37/64 = .5625	29/32 = .90625
17/64 = .265625	19/32 = .578125	59/64 = .921875
9/32 = .28125	39/64 = .59375	15/16 = .9375
19/64 = .296875	5/8 = .609375	61/64 = .953125
5/16 = .3125	41/64 = .625	31/32 = .96875
21/64 = .328125	21/32 = .640625	63/64 = .984375

The decimal equivalents of common fractions given in Table 3 will be found very useful.

RATIO AND PROPORTION

A ratio is virtually a fraction. When two ratios are equal, the four terms form a proportion. Thus 2:4::3:6, which is read as, 2 is to 4 as 3 is to 6. Sometimes the = sign is placed between the two ratios instead of the sign ::, thus 2:4=3:6.

Rule—Two quantities of *different* kinds cannot form the terms of a ratio.

Rule—The product of the extremes equals the product of the means.

Example:

$$4:8 = 2:4; \text{ or } 4 \times 4 = 8 \times 2, \text{ or } 16 = 16$$

Rule of Three—When three terms of a proportion are given, the method of finding the fourth term is called the *rule of three*.

Example—If five bundles of shingles cost $16, what will 25 bundles cost? Let X equal the unknown term; then

$$5 \text{ bundles}: 25 \text{ bundles} = \$16 : \$X.$$

$$5 \times X = 25 \times 16$$

$$X = \frac{25 \times 16}{5} = \$80$$

PERCENTAGE

A profit of 6% means a gain of $6 on every $100. Note carefully with respect to the symbol %. 5% means 5/100 which, when reduced to a decimal (as is necessary in making a calculation), becomes .05. However, .05% has a quite different value; thus, .05% means .05/100 which, when reduced to a decimal, becomes .0005; that is, 5/100 of 1%.

Rule—If the decimal has more than two places, the figures that follow the hundredths place signify parts of 1%.

Example—If the list price of shingles is $16 per 1000, what is the net cost with 5% discount for cash?

$$5\% = \frac{5}{100} = .05; \ 16 \times .05 = 80\cent; \ \$16 - 80\cent = \$15.20$$

POWERS OF NUMBERS

The *square* of a number is its second power; the *cube,* its third power. Thus,

the square of $2 = 2 \times 2 = 4$; the cube of $2 = 2 \times 2 \times 2 = 8$

The power to which a number is raised is indicated by a small *superior* figure called an *exponent*. Thus,

$$2^2 = 2 \times 2 = 4; \ 2^3 = 2 \times 2 \times 2 = 8$$

29

ROOTS OF NUMBERS (EVOLUTION)

In the equation $2 \times 2 = 4$, the number 2 is the root for which the power (4) is produced. The radical sign $\sqrt{}$ placed over a number means the root of the number is to be extracted. Thus $\sqrt{4}$ means that the square root of 4 is to be extracted. The *index* of the root is a small figure placed over the radical.

Rule—(Square Root). As shown in the example, point off the given number into groups of two places each, beginning with units. If there are decimals, point these off likewise, beginning at the decimal point and supplying as many ciphers as may be needed. Find the greatest number whose square is less than the first left-hand group, and place it as the first figure in the quotient. Subtract its square from the left-hand group, and annex the two figures of the second group to the remainder for a dividend. Double the first figure of the quotient for a partial divisor; find how many times the latter is contained in the dividend, exclusive of the right-hand figure in the quotient, and annex it to the right of the partial divisor, forming the complete divisor. Multiply this divisor by the second figure in the quotient, and subtract the product from the dividend. To the remainder, bring down the next group and proceed as before, in each case doubling the figures in the root already found to obtain the trial divisor. Should the product of the second figure in the root by the completed divisor be greater than the dividend, erase the second figure both from the quotient and from the divisor, and substitute the next smaller figure, or one small enough to make the product of the second figure by the divisor less than or equal to the dividend.

Rule—(Cube root). As shown in the example, separate the number into groups of three figures each, beginning at the units. Find the greatest cube in the left-hand group and write its root for the first figure of the required root. Cube this root, subtract the result from the left-hand group, and to the remainder annex the next group for a dividend. For a partial divisor, take three times the square of the root already found (considered as tens), and divide the dividend by it. The quotient (or the quotient

Example:

$$3.1\overset{\bullet}{4}1\overset{\bullet}{5}9\overset{\bullet}{2}6\overset{\bullet}{5}36 \lfloor 1.77245+$$

```
3.14159265.36| 1.77245+
         1
     27|214
       |189
     347|2515
        |2429
    3542|8692
        |7084
   35444|160865
        |141776
  354485|1908936
        |1772425
```

diminished) will be the second figure of the root. To this partial divisor add three times the product of the first figure on the root (considered as tens) by the second figure, and also the square of the second figure. This sum will be the complete divisor. Multiply the complete divisor by the second figure of the root, subtract the product from the dividend, and to the remainder annex the next group for a new dividend. Proceed in this manner until all the groups have been annexed. The result will be the cube root required. Table 4 can be a great help in determining the square, cube, square root, or cube root of numbers up to 100.

Table 4. Squares, Cubes, Square Roots, and Cube Roots

No.	Square	Cube	Square Root	Cube Root	Reciprocal
1	1	1	1.00000	1.00000	1.00000
2	4	8	1.41421	1.25992	.50000
3	9	27	1.73205	1.44224	.33333
4	16	64	2.00000	1.58740	.25000
5	25	125	2.23606	1.70997	.20000
6	36	216	2.44948	1.81712	.16666
7	49	343	2.64575	1.91293	.14285
8	64	512	2.82842	2.00000	.12500
9	81	729	3.00000	2.08008	.11111
10	100	1000	3.16227	2.15443	.10000

Table 4. Squares, Cubes, Square and Cube Roots (Cont'd)

No.	Square	Cube	Square Root	Cube Root	Reciprocal
11	121	1331	3.31662	2.22398	.09090
12	144	1728	3.46410	2.28942	.08333
13	169	2197	3.60555	2.35133	.07602
14	196	2744	3.74165	2.41014	.07142
15	225	3375	3.87298	2.46621	.06666
16	256	4096	4.00000	2.51984	.06250
17	289	4913	4.12310	2.57128	.05882
18	324	5832	4.24264	2.62074	.05555
19	361	6859	4.35889	2.66840	.05263
20	400	8000	4.47213	2.71441	.05000
21	441	9621	4.58257	2.75892	.04761
22	484	10648	4.69041	2.80203	.04545
23	529	12167	4.79583	2.84386	.04347
24	576	13824	4.89897	2.88449	.04166
25	625	15625	5.00000	2.92401	.04000
26	676	17576	5.09901	2.96249	.03846
27	729	19683	5.19615	3.00000	.03703
28	784	21952	5.29150	3.03658	.03571
29	841	24389	5.38516	3.07231	.03448
30	900	27000	5.47722	3.10723	.03333
31	961	29791	5.56776	3.14138	.03225
32	1024	32768	5.65685	3.17480	.03125
33	1089	35937	5.74456	3.20753	.03030
34	1156	39304	5.83095	3.23961	.02941
35	1225	42875	5.91607	3.27106	.02857
36	1296	46656	6.00000	3.30192	.02777
37	1369	50653	6.08276	3.33222	.02702
38	1444	54872	6.16441	3.36197	.02631
39	1521	59319	6.24499	3.39121	.02564
40	1600	64000	6.32455	3.41995	.02500
41	1681	68921	6.40312	3.44821	.02439
42	1764	74088	6.48074	3.47602	.02380
43	1849	79507	6.55743	3.50339	.02325
44	1936	85184	6.63324	3.53034	.02272
45	2025	91125	6.70820	3.55689	.02222
46	2116	97336	6.78233	3.58304	.02173
47	2209	103823	6.85565	3.60882	.02127
48	2304	110592	6.92820	3.63424	.02083
49	2401	117649	7.00000	3.65930	.02040
50	2500	125000	7.07106	3.68403	.02000
51	2601	132651	7.14142	3.70842	.01960
52	2704	140608	7.21110	3.73251	.01923
53	2809	148877	7.28010	3.75628	.01886
54	2916	157464	7.34846	3.77976	.01851
55	3025	166375	7.41619	3.80295	.01818

Table 4. Squares, Cubes, Square and Cube Roots (Cont'd)

No.	Square	Cube	Square Root	Cube Root	Reciprocal
56	3136	175616	7.48331	3.82586	.01785
57	3249	185193	7.54983	3.84850	.01754
58	3364	195112	7.61577	3.87087	.01724
59	3481	205379	7.68114	3.89299	.01694
60	3600	216000	7.74596	3.91486	.01666
61	3721	226981	7.81024	3.93649	.01639
62	3844	238328	7.87400	3.95789	.01612
63	3969	250047	7.93725	3.97905	.01587
64	4096	262144	8.00000	4.00000	.01562
65	4225	274625	8.06225	4.02072	.01538
66	4356	287496	8.12403	4.04124	.01515
67	4489	300763	8.18535	4.06154	.01492
68	4624	314432	8.24621	4.08165	.01470
69	4761	328500	8.30662	4.10156	.01449
70	4900	343000	8.36660	4.12128	.01428
71	5041	357911	8.42614	4.14081	.01408
72	5184	373248	8.48528	4.16016	.01388
73	5329	389017	8.54400	4.17933	.01369
74	5476	405224	8.60232	4.19833	.01351
75	5625	421875	8.66025	4.21716	.01333
76	5776	438976	8.71779	4.23582	.01315
77	5929	456533	8.77496	4.25432	.01298
78	6084	474552	8.83176	4.27265	.01282
79	6241	493039	8.88819	4.29084	.01265
80	6400	512000	8.94427	4.30886	.01250
81	6561	531441	9.00000	4.32674	.01234
82	6724	551368	9.05538	4.34448	.01219
83	6889	571787	9.11043	4.36207	.01204
84	7056	592704	9.16515	4.37951	.01190
85	7225	614125	9.21954	4.39682	.01176
86	7396	636056	9.27361	4.41400	.01162
87	7569	658503	9.32737	4.43104	.01149
88	7744	681472	9.38083	4.44796	.01136
89	7921	704969	9.43398	4.46474	.01123
90	8100	729000	9.48683	4.48140	.01111
91	8281	753571	9.53939	4.49794	.01098
92	8464	778688	9.59166	4.51435	.01086
93	8649	804357	9.64365	4.53065	.01075
94	8836	830584	9.69535	4.54683	.01063
95	9025	857375	9.74679	4.56290	.01052
96	9216	884736	9.79795	4.57885	.01041
97	9409	912673	9.84885	4.59470	.01030
98	9604	941192	9.89949	4.61043	.01020
99	9801	970299	9.94987	4.62606	.01010
100	10000	1000000	10.00000	4.64158	.01000

Example:

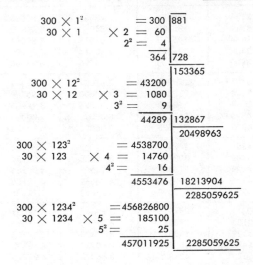

$$1,881,365,963,625 \ | \ 12345$$

$$
\begin{array}{ll}
300 \times 1^2 & = 300 \ \rfloor 881 \\
30 \times 1 \quad \times 2 = 60 \\
2^2 = \underline{4} \\
 364 \ \rfloor 728
\end{array}
$$

153365

$$
\begin{array}{ll}
300 \times 12^2 & = 43200 \\
30 \times 12 \quad \times 3 = 1080 \\
3^2 = \underline{9} \\
 44289 \ | 132867
\end{array}
$$

20498963

$$
\begin{array}{ll}
300 \times 123^2 & = 4538700 \\
30 \times 123 \quad \times 4 = 14760 \\
4^2 = \underline{16} \\
 4553476 \ | \ 18213904
\end{array}
$$

2285059625

$$
\begin{array}{ll}
300 \times 1234^2 & = 456826800 \\
30 \times 1234 \quad \times 5 = 185100 \\
5^2 = \underline{25} \\
 457011925 \ | \ 2285059625
\end{array}
$$

Rule—(Roots higher than the cube). The fourth root is the square root of the square root; the sixth root is the cube root of the square root, or the square root of the cube root. Other roots are most conveniently found by the use of logarithims.

THE METRIC SYSTEM

The important feature of the metric system is that it is based upon the *decimal scale.* Thus, the student should first acquire a knowledge of decimals before taking up this system.

The metric system is the decimal system of measures and weights, with the meter and the gram as the bases. The unit of length (the meter) was intended to be, and is very nearly one ten-millionth part of the distance measured on a meridian from the equator to the pole, or 39.37079 inches. The other primary units of measure such as the *square meter,* the *cubic meter,* the *liter,* and the *gram* are based on the meter.

Following is the *metric* system of weights and measures. Table 5 shows the conversion of millimeters into inches, and Table 6 shows the conversion of inches into millimeters.

Milli expresses the 1000th part.
Centi expresses the 100th part.
Deci expresses the 10th part.
Deka expresses 10 times the value.
Hecto expresses 100 times the value.
Kilo expresses 1000 times the value.

Length

1 mm. = 1 Millimeter = 1/1000 of a meter =	.03937	in.
10 mm. = 1 Centimeter = 1/100 of a meter =	.3937	in.
10 cm. = 1 Decimeter = 1/10 of a meter =	3.937	in.
10 dm. = 1 Meter = 1 meter =	39.37	in.
10 m. = 1 Dekameter = 10 meters =	32.8	ft.
10 Dm. = 1 Hectometer = 100 meters =	328.09	ft.
10 Hm. = 1 Kilometer = 1000 meters =	.62137	mile.

Square Measure

1 sq. centimeter = 0.1550 sq. in.   1 sq. in. = 6.452 sq. centimeters
1 sq. decimeter = 0.1076 sq. ft.   1 sq. ft. = 9.2903 sq. decimeters
1 sq. meter = 1.196 sq. yd.   1 sq. yd. = 0.8361 sq. meter
1 are = 3.954 sq. rd.   1 sq. rd. = 0.2529 are
1 hektar = 2.47 acres   1 acre = 0.4047 hektar
1 sq. kilometer = 0.386 sq. mile   1 sq. mile = 2.59 sq. kilometers

Table Weights

1 gram = 0.0527 ounce   1 ounce = 28.35 grams
1 kilogram = 2.2046 lbs.   1 lb. = 0.4536 kilogram
1 metric ton = 1.1023 English   1 English ton = 0.9072 metric
  ton   ton

Approximate Metric Equivalents

1 decimeter = 4 inches   1 hektar = 2-1/2 acres
1 meter = 1.1 yards   1 stere or cu. meter = 1/4
1 kilometer = 5/8 mile   cord

Approximate Metric Equivalents (Cont'd)

1 liter = 1.06 qt. liquid; 0.9 qt. dry

1 hektoliter = 2-5/8 bushel

1 kilogram = 2-1/5 lbs.

1 metric ton = 2200 lbs.

Long Measure

12 inches (in. or ″)	= 1 foot (ft. or ′)
3 feet	= 1 yard (yd.)
5-1/2 yards or 16-1/2 feet	= 1 rod (rd.)
40 rods	= 1 furlong (fur.)
8 furlongs or 320 rods	= 1 statute mile (mi.)

Nautical Measure

6080.26 ft. or 1.15156 statute miles = 1 nautical mile

3 nautical miles = 1 league

60 nautical miles or 69.168 statute miles = 1 degree (at the equator)

360 degrees = circumference of earth at equator

Square Measure

144 square inches (sq. in.) = 1 square foot (sq. ft.)

9 sq. ft. = 1 square yard (sq. yd.)

30-1/4 sq. yd. = 1 square rod or perch (sq. rd. or P.)

640 acres = 1 square mile (sq. mi.)

MENSURATION

Mensuration is the process of measuring objects which occupy space; for instance, finding the length of a line, area of triangle, the volume of a cube, etc.

Table 5. Millimeters to Inches

mm.	inches		mm.	inches		mm.	inches
1/50 = .00079			26/50 = .02047			2 = .07874	
2/50 = .00157			27/50 = .02126			3 = .11811	
3/50 = .00236			28/50 = .02205			4 = .15748	
4/50 = .00315			29/50 = .02283			5 = .19685	
5/50 = .00394			30/50 = .02362			6 = .23622	
6/50 = .00472			31/50 = .02441			7 = .27559	
7/50 = .00551			32/50 = .02520			8 = .31496	
8/50 = .00630			33/50 = .02598			9 = .35433	
9/50 = .00709			34/50 = .02677			10 = .39370	
10/50 = .00787			35/50 = .02756			11 = .43307	
11/50 = .00866			36/50 = .02835			12 = .47244	
12/50 = .00945			37/50 = .02913			13 = .51181	
13/50 = .01024			38/50 = .02992			14 = .55118	
14/50 = .01102			39/50 = .03071			15 = .59055	
15/50 = .01181			40/50 = .03150			16 = .62992	
16/50 = .01260			41/50 = .03228			17 = .66929	
17/50 = .01339			42/50 = .03307			18 = .70866	
18/50 = .01417			43/50 = .03386			19 = .74803	
19/50 = .01496			44/50 = .03465			20 = .78740	
20/50 = .01575			45/50 = .03543			21 = .82677	
21/50 = .01654			46/50 = .03622			22 = .86614	
22/50 = .01732			47/50 = .03701			23 = .90551	
23/50 = .01811			48/50 = .03780			24 = .94488	
24/50 = .01890			49/50 = .03858			25 = .98425	
25/50 = .01969			1 = .03937			26 = 1.02362	

Triangles

Figures bounded by three sides are called triangles; there are numerous kinds due to varying the angles and length of sides.

To find the length of the hypotenuse of a right triangle.
Rule—The hypotenuse is equal to the square root of the sum of the squares of each leg, as shown in Fig. 1.

To find the length of either leg of a right triangle.
Rule—Either leg is equal to the square root of the difference between the square of the hypotenuse and the square of the other leg (Fig. 1).

To find the area of any triangle.
Rule—Multiply the base by half the perpendicular height. Thus, if the base is 12 ft. and the height 8 ft., the area = 1/2 of 8 × 12 = 48 sq. ft.

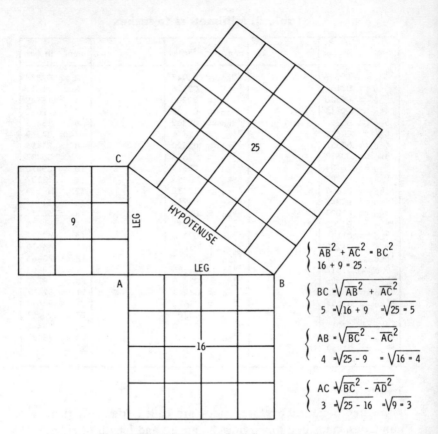

$$\begin{cases} \overline{AB}^2 + \overline{AC}^2 = \overline{BC}^2 \\ 16 + 9 = 25 \end{cases}$$

$$\begin{cases} BC = \sqrt{\overline{AB}^2 + \overline{AC}^2} \\ 5 = \sqrt{16 + 9} = \sqrt{25} = 5 \end{cases}$$

$$\begin{cases} AB = \sqrt{\overline{BC}^2 - \overline{AC}^2} \\ 4 = \sqrt{25 - 9} = \sqrt{16} = 4 \end{cases}$$

$$\begin{cases} AC = \sqrt{\overline{BC}^2 - \overline{AD}^2} \\ 3 = \sqrt{25 - 16} = \sqrt{9} = 3 \end{cases}$$

Fig. 1. Right triangle showing mathematical relations.

Quadrilaterals

Any plain figure bounded by four sides is a quadrilateral, as shown in Fig. 2.

To find the area of a trapezium.

Rule—Join two of its opposite angles, and thus divide it into two triangles. Measure this line and call it the base of each triangle. Measure the perpendicular height of each triangle above the base line. Then find the area of each triangle by the previous rule; their sum is the area of the whole figure.

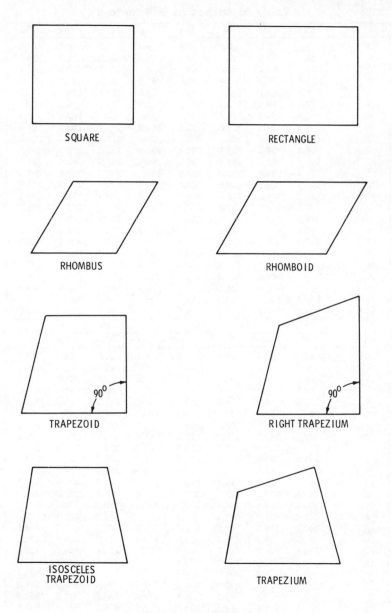

SQUARE

RECTANGLE

RHOMBUS

RHOMBOID

TRAPEZOID

RIGHT TRAPEZIUM

ISOSCELES
TRAPEZOID

TRAPEZIUM

Fig. 2. Various quadrilaterals.

Table 6. Inches to Millimeters

In.	0	1/16	1/8	3/16	7/16	1/4	5/16	3/8
0	0.0	1.6	3.2	4.8	6.4	7.9	9.5	11.1
1	25.4	27.0	28.6	30.2	31.7	33.3	34.9	36.5
2	50.8	52.4	54.0	55.6	57.1	58.7	60.3	61.9
3	76.2	77.8	79.4	81.0	82.5	84.1	85.7	87.3
4	101.6	103.2	104.8	106.4	108.0	109.5	111.1	112.7
5	127.0	128.6	130.2	131.8	133.4	134.9	136.5	138.1
6	152.4	154.0	155.6	157.2	158.8	160.3	161.9	163.5
7	177.8	179.4	181.0	182.6	184.2	185.7	187.3	188.9
8	203.2	204.8	206.4	208.0	209.6	211.1	212.7	214.3
9	228.6	230.2	231.8	233.4	235.0	236.5	238.1	239.7
10	254.0	255.6	257.2	258.8	260.4	261.9	263.5	265.1
11	279.4	281.0	282.6	284.2	285.7	287.3	288.9	290.5
12	304.8	306.4	308.0	309.6	311.1	312.7	314.3	315.9
13	330.2	331.8	333.4	335.0	336.5	338.1	339.7	341.3
14	355.6	357.2	358.8	360.4	361.9	363.5	365.1	366.7
15	381.0	382.6	384.2	385.8	387.3	388.9	390.5	392.1
16	406.4	408.0	409.6	411.2	412.7	414.3	415.9	417.5
17	431.8	433.4	435.0	436.6	438.1	439.7	441.3	442.9
18	457.2	458.8	460.4	462.0	463.5	465.1	466.7	468.3
19	482.6	484.2	485.8	487.4	488.9	490.5	492.1	493.7
20	508.0	509.6	511.2	512.8	514.3	515.9	517.5	519.1
21	533.4	535.0	536.6	538.2	539.7	541.3	542.9	544.5
22	558.8	560.4	562.0	563.6	565.1	566.7	568.3	569.9
23	584.2	585.8	587.4	589.0	590.5	592.1	593.7	595.3

In.	1/2	9/16	5/8	11/16	3/4	13/16	7/8	15/16
0	12.7	14.3	15.9	17.5	19.1	20.6	22.2	23.8
1	38.1	39.7	41.3	42.9	44.4	46.0	47.6	49.2
2	63.5	65.1	66.7	68.3	69.8	71.4	73.0	74.6
3	88.9	90.5	92.1	93.7	95.2	96.8	98.4	100.0
4	114.3	115.9	117.5	119.1	120.7	122.2	123.8	125.4
5	139.7	141.3	142.9	144.5	146.1	147.6	149.2	150.8
6	165.1	166.7	168.3	169.9	171.5	173.0	174.6	176.2
7	190.5	192.1	193.7	195.3	196.9	198.4	200.0	201.6
8	215.9	217.5	219.1	220.7	222.3	223.8	225.4	227.0
9	241.3	242.9	244.5	246.1	247.7	249.2	250.8	252.4
10	266.7	268.3	269.9	271.5	273.1	274.6	276.2	277.8
11	292.1	293.7	295.3	296.9	298.4	300.0	301.6	303.2
12	317.5	319.1	320.7	322.3	323.8	325.4	327.0	328.6
13	342.9	344.5	346.1	347.7	349.2	350.8	352.4	354.0
14	368.3	369.9	371.5	373.1	374.6	376.2	377.8	379.4
15	393.7	395.3	396.9	398.5	400.0	401.6	403.2	404.8
16	419.1	420.7	422.3	423.9	425.4	427.0	428.6	430.2
17	444.5	446.1	447.7	449.3	450.8	452.4	454.0	455.6
18	469.9	471.5	473.1	474.7	476.2	477.8	479.4	481.0
19	495.3	496.9	498.5	500.1	501.6	503.2	504.8	506.4
20	520.7	522.3	523.9	525.5	527.0	528.6	530.2	531.8
21	546.1	547.7	549.3	550.9	552.4	554.0	555.6	557.2
22	571.5	573.1	574.7	576.3	577.8	579.4	581.0	582.6
23	596.9	598.5	600.1	601.7	603.2	604.8	606.4	608.0

To find the area of a trapezoid.

Rule—Multiply half the sum of the two parallel sides by the perpendicular distance between them.

To find the area of a square.

Rule—Multiply the base by the height; that is, multiply the length by the breadth.

To find the area of a rectangle.

Rule—Multiply the length by the breadth.

To find the area of a parallelogram.

Rule—Multiply the base by the perpendicular height.

Polygons

These comprise the numerous figures having more than four sides, named according to the number of sides, thus:

> pentagon . . 5 sides
> hexagon . . . 6 sides
> heptagon . . 7 sides
> octagon . . . 8 sides
> nonagon . . 9 sides
> decagon . . 10 sides

To find the area of a polygon.

Rule—Multiply the sum of the sides (perimeter of the polygon) by the perpendicular dropped from its center to one of its sides, and half the product will be the area. This rule applies to all regular polygons.

To find the area of any regular polygon when the length of a side only is given.

Rule—Multiply the square of the sides by the figure for "area when side = 1" opposite the polygon in Table 7.

Table 7. Table of Regular Polygons

Number of sides	3	4	5	6	7	8	9	10	11	12
Area when side = 1	.433	1.	1.721	2.598	3.634	4.828	6.181	7.694	9.366	11.196

The Circle

The Greek letter π (called pi) is used to represent 3.1416, the circumference of a circle whose diameter is 1. The circumference of a circle equals the diameter multiplied by 3.1416. The reason why the decimal .78543 is used to calculate the area of a circle is explained in Fig. 3.

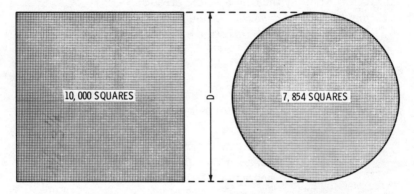

Fig. 3. Diagram illustrating why the decimal .7854 is used to find the area of a circle.

To find the circumference of a circle.

Rule—Multiply the diameter by 3.1416.

To find the diameter of a circle (circumference given).

Rule—Divide the circumference by 3.1416.

To find the area of a circle.

Rule—Multiply the square of the diameter by .7854. (See Fig. 3.)

To find the diameter of a circle (area given).

Rule—Extract the square root of the area divided by .7854.

To find the area of a sector of a circle.

Rule—Multiply the arc of the sector by half the radius.

To find the area of a segment of a circle.

Rule—Find the area of the sector which has the same arc and also the area of the triangle formed by the radii and chord; take the sum of these areas if the segment is greater than 1800; take the difference if less.

To find the area of a ring.

Rule—Take the difference between the areas of the two circles.

To find the area of an ellipse.

Rule—Multiply the product of the two diameters by .7854.

Relation of a circle to an equal, inscribed, and circumscribed square.

Diameter of circle	$\times$ .88623	$\Big\}=$ side of equal square
Circumference of circle	$\times$ .28209	
Circumference of circle	$\times$ 1.1284	= perimeter of equal square
Diameter of circle	$\times$ .7071	$\Big\}=$ side of inscribed square
Circumference of circle	$\times$ .22508	
Area of circle	$\times$ .90031 ÷ diameter	
Area of circle	$\times$ 1.2732	= area of circumscribed square
Area of circle	$\times$ .63662	= area of inscribed square
Side of square	$\times$ 1.4142	= diam. of circumscribed circle
Side of square	$\times$ 4.4428	= circum.
Side of square	$\times$ 1.1284	= diam. of equal circle
Side of square	$\times$ 3.5449	= circum. of equal circle
Perimeter of square	$\times$ .88623	= circum. of equal circle
Square inches	$\times$ 1.2732	= circular inches

43

Solids

Finding the volume of solids involves the multiplication of three dimensions—length, breadth and thickness;

To find the volume of a solid.
Rule—Multiply the area of the base by the perpendicular height.

To find the volume of a rectangular solid.
Rule—Multiply the length, breadth, and height.

To find the surface of a cylinder.
Rule—Multiply 3.1416 by the diameter times the length.

To find the volume of a cylinder.
Rule—Multiply .7854 by the diameter squared of the base times the length of the cylinder.

To find the surface of a sphere.
Rule—Multiply the area of its great circle by 4.

To find the volume of a sphere.
Rule—Multiply .7854 by the cube of the diameter, and then take 2/3 of the product.

To find the volume of a segment of a sphere.
Rule—To three times the square of the radius of the segment's base, add the square of the depth or height; then multiply this sum by the depth, and the product by .5236.

To find the surface of a cylindrical ring.
Rule—To the thickness of the ring, add the inner diameter; multiply this sum by the thickness, and the product again by 9.8696.

To find the volume of a cylindrical ring.
Rule—To the thickness of the ring, add the inner diameter; multiply this sum by the square of the thickness, and the product again by 2.4674.

To find the slant area of a cone.
Rule—Multiply 3.1416 by the diameter of the base and by one-half the slant height.

To find the slant area of the frustrum of a cone.
Rule—Multiply half the slant height by the sum of the circumferences.

To find the volume of a cone.

Rule—Multiply the area of the base by the perpendicular height, and by 1/3.

To find the volume of a frustum of a cone.

Rule—Find the sum of the squares of the two diameters (d, D), and add to this the product of the two diameters multiplied by .7854, and by one-third the height (h).

To find the volume of a pyramid.

Rule—Multiply the area of the base by one-third of the perpendicular height.

To find the volume of a rectangular solid.

Rule—Multiply the length, breadth, and thickness.

To find the volume of a rectangular wedge.

Rule—Find the area of one of the triangular ends and multiply by the distance between ends.

Mensuration of Surfaces and Volumes

Area of rectangle = length × breadth.
Area of triangle = base × 1/2 perpendicular height.
Diameter of circle = radius × 2.
Circumference of circle = diameter × 3.1416.
Area of circle = square of diameter × .7854.
Area of sector of circle =

$$\frac{\text{area of circle} \times \text{number of degrees in arc}}{360}$$

Area of surface of cylinder = circumference × length + area of two ends.

To find diameter of circle having given area: Divide the area by .7854, and extract the square root.

To find the volume of a cylinder: Multiply the area of the section in square inches by the length in inches = the volume in cubic inches. Cubic inches divided by 1728 = volume in cubic feet.

Surface of a sphere = square of diameter × 3.1416.
Volume of a sphere = cube of diameter × .5236.
Side of an inscribed cube = radius of a sphere × 1.1547.

Area of the base of a pyramid or cone, whether round, square or triangular, multiplied by one-third of its height = the volume.

Diam. $\times$ .8862 = side of an equal square.
Diam. $\times$ .7071 = side of an inscribed square.
Radius $\times$ 6.2832 = circumference.
Circumference = 3.5446 $\times \sqrt{\text{Area of circle}}$.
Diameter = 1.1283 $\times \sqrt{\text{Area of circle}}$.
Length of arc = No. of degrees $\times$ .017453 radius.
Degrees in arc whose length equals radius = 57° 2958′.
Length of an arc of 1° = radius $\times$ .017453.
Length of an arc of 1 Min. = radius $\times$ .0002909.
Length of an arc of 1 Sec. = radius $\times$ .0000048.

π = Proportion of circumference to diameter = 3.1415926.

π^2 = 9.8696044.

$\sqrt{\pi}$ = 1.7724538.

$\text{Log}\pi$ = 0.49715.

$\dfrac{1}{\pi}$ = 0.31831.

1/360 = .002778.

$\dfrac{360}{\pi}$ = 114.59.

Lineal feet	$\times$	.00019	= Miles.
Lineal yards	$\times$	.0006	= Miles.
Square inches	$\times$	.007	= Square feet.
Square feet	$\times$	.111	= Square yards.
Square yards	$\times$	.0002067	= Acres.
Acres	$\times$	4840	= Square yards.
Cubic inches	$\times$	.00058	= Cubic feet.
Cubic feet	$\times$	.03704	= Cubic yards.
Circular inches	$\times$	.00546	= Square feet.
Cyl. inches	$\times$	.0004546	= Cubic feet.
Cyl. feet	$\times$	.02909	= Cubic yards.
Links	$\times$	.22	= Yards.
Links	$\times$	.66	= Feet.
Feet	$\times$	1.5	= Links.

Width in chains ....×	8	= Acres per mile.
Cubic feet ....×	7.48	= U. S. gallons.
Cubic inches ....×	.004329	= U. S. gallons.
U. S. gallons ....×	.13367	= Cubic feet.
U. S. gallons ....×	231	= Cubic inches.
Cubic feet ....×	.8036	= U. S. bushel.
Cubic inches. ....×	.000466	= U. S. bushel.
Lbs. Avoir ....×	.009	= cwt. (112)
Lbs. Avoir ....×	.00045	= Tons (2240)
Cubic feet of water ....×	62.5	= Lbs. Avoir.
Cubic inch of water ....×	.03617	= Lbs. Avoir.
13.44 U. S. gallons of water		= 1 cwt.
268.8 U. S. gallons of water		= 1 ton.
1.8 cubic feet of water		= 1 cwt.
35.88 cubic feet of water		= 1 ton.
Column of water, 12 inches high, and 1 inch in diameter		= .341 Lbs.
U. S. bushel ....×	.0495	= Cubic yards.
U. S. bushel ....×	1.2446	= Cubic feet.
U. S. bushel ....× 2150.42		= inches.

To find the volume of irregular solids.

Rule—Divide the irregular solid into different figures; and the sum of their volumes, found by the preceding problems, will be the volume required. If the figures is a compound solid, whose two ends are equal plane figures, the volume may be found by multiplying the area of one end by the length. To find the volume of a piece of wood or stone that is craggy or uneven, put it into a tub or cistern, and pour in as much water as will just cover it; then take it out and find the contents of that part of the vessel through which the water has descended and it will be the volume required.

To find the surface and volume of any of the five regular solids shown in Fig. 4.

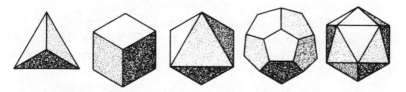

Fig. 4. Illustrating the five regular solids.

47

Rule—(surface) Multiply the area given in Table 8 by the square of the edge of the solid.

Rule—(volume) Multiply the contents given in Table 8 by the cube of the given edge.

Table 8. Surfaces and Volumes of Regular Solids

Number of Sides	Name	Area Edge = 1	Contents Edge = 1
4	................Tetrahedron...................	1.7320	0.1178
6	................Hexahedron...................	6.0000	1.0000
8	................Octahedron...................	3.4641	0.4714
12	................Dodecahedron...............	20.6458	7.6631
20	................Icosahedron...................	8.6603	2.1817

TRIGONOMETRIC FUNCTIONS

Every triangle has only six parts—3 sides and 3 angles. When any three of these parts are given (provided one of them is a side), the other parts may be determined. Fig. 5 illustrates the

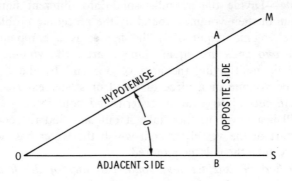

Fig. 5. Illustrating a triangle, A O B, for expressing trigonometric functions as ratios.

parts considered in expressing trigonometric functions. It will be noted in this triangle that angle ABO = 90°. In this triangle the trigonometric functions, expressed as ratios, are as follows:

$$\textit{Sine} \text{ of the angle} = \frac{AB}{AO} = \frac{\text{opposite side}}{\text{hypotenuse}}$$

$$\textit{Cosine} \text{ of the angle} \quad = \frac{OB}{OA} = \frac{\text{adjacent side}}{\text{hypotenuse}}$$

$$\textit{Tangent} \text{ of the angle} \quad = \frac{AB}{OB} = \frac{\text{opposite side}}{\text{adjacent side}}$$

$$\textit{Cotangent} \text{ of the angle} \quad = \frac{OB}{AB} = \frac{\text{adjacent side}}{\text{opposite side}}$$

$$\textit{Secant} \text{ of the angle} \quad = \frac{OA}{OB} = \frac{\text{hypotenuse}}{\text{adjacent side}}$$

$$\textit{Cosecant} \text{ of the angle} \quad = \frac{OA}{AB} = \frac{\text{hypotenuse}}{\text{opposite side}}$$

Natural Functions

These are virtually ratios, but by taking what corresponds to the hypotenuse OA, in the triangle AOB in Fig. 5, as a radius of unity length of a circle the denominators of the ratios are unity or 1. These denominators disappear, leaving only the numerators;

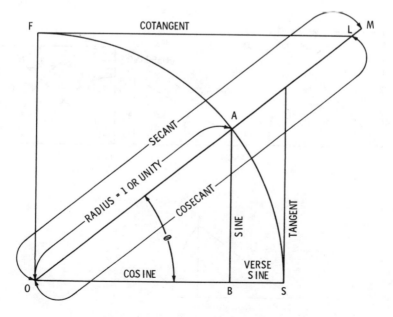

Fig. 6. Natural trigonometric functions.

that is, a line instead of a ratio or function. These lines are the so-called *natural functions*. Thus, in Fig. 6:

$$\textit{Sine} \text{ angle } = \frac{AB}{radius} = \frac{AB}{1} = AB$$

$$\textit{Cosine} \text{ angle } = \frac{radius}{OB} = OB$$

$$\textit{Tangent} \text{ angle } = \frac{MS}{OS} = \frac{MS}{radius} = MS$$

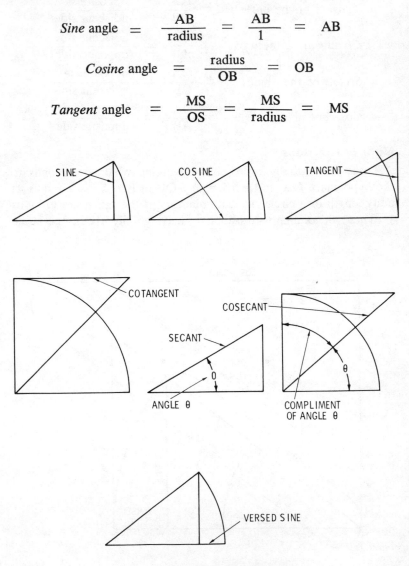

Fig. 7. Illustrating trigonometric shapes.

Cotangent angle = *tangent* of complement of angle

$$= \frac{OM}{OF} = \frac{OM}{radius} = OM$$

$$Secant\ angle = \frac{OM}{OS} = \frac{OM}{radius} = OM$$

Cosecant angle = *secant* of complement angle =

$$\frac{OL}{OF} = \frac{OL}{radius} = OL$$

The natural trigonometric functions which are shown in Fig. 7 are the ones of value in ordinary calculations and should be thoroughly understood. They are used in connection with Table 9, as illustrated by the following example.

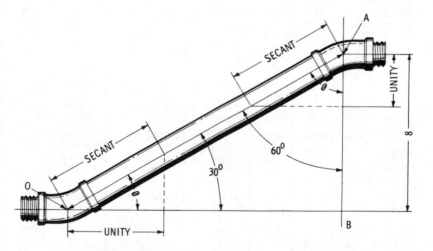

Fig. 8. Two parallel pipe lines connected with 30° elbows illustrating the use of natural trigonometric functions in finding the offset and length of connecting pipes.

Example—In Fig. 8, two pipe lines 8 in. apart are to be connected with 30° elbows. What is the length of the offset OB and connecting pipe OA? From Table 9, tangent 60° = 1.73; length offset OB = 1.73 × 8 = 13.84. Again, from Table 9 secant 60° = 2; length connecting pipe OA = 8 × 2 = 16 ins.

Table 9.   Natural Trigonometric Functions

Degs.	Sine	Cosine	Tangent	Secant	Degs.	Sine	Cosine	Tangent	Secant
0	.00000	1.0000	.00000	1.0000	46	.7193	.6947	1.0355	1.4395
1	.01745	.9998	.01745	1.0001	47	.7314	.6820	1.0724	1.4663
2	.03490	.9994	.03492	1.0006	48	.7431	.6691	1.1106	1.4945
3	.05234	.9986	.05241	1.0014	49	.7547	.6561	1.1504	1.5242
4	.06976	.9976	.06993	1.0024	50	.7660	.6428	1.1918	1.5557
5	.08716	.9962	.08749	1.0038	51	.7771	.6293	1.2349	1.5890
6	.10453	.9945	.10510	1.0055	52	.7880	.6157	1.2799	1.6243
7	.12187	.9925	.12278	1.0075	53	.7986	.6018	1.3270	1.6616
8	.1392	.9903	.1405	1.0098	54	.8090	.5878	1.3764	1.7013
9	.1564	.9877	.1584	1.0125	55	.8192	.5736	1.4281	1.7434
10	.1736	.9848	.1763	1.0154	56	.8290	.5592	1.4826	1.7883
11	.1908	.9816	.1944	1.0187	57	.8387	.5446	1.5399	1.8361
12	.2079	.9781	.2126	1.0223	58	.8480	.5299	1.6003	1.8871
13	.2250	.9744	.2309	1.0263	59	.8572	.5150	1.6643	1.9416
14	.2419	.9703	.2493	1.0306	60	.8660	.5000	1.7321	2.0000
15	.2588	.9659	.2679	1.0353	61	.8746	.4848	1.8040	2.0627
16	.2756	.9613	.2867	1.0403	62	.8829	.4695	1.8807	2.1300
17	.2924	.9563	.3057	1.0457	63	.8910	.4540	1.9626	2.2027
18	.3090	.9511	.3249	1.0515	64	.8988	.4384	2.0503	2.2812
19	.3256	.9455	.3443	1.0576	65	.9063	.4226	2.1445	2.3662
20	.3420	.9397	.3640	1.0642	66	.9135	.4067	2.2460	2.4586
21	.3584	.9336	.3839	1.0711	67	.9205	.3907	2.3559	2.5593
22	.3746	.9272	.4040	1.0785	68	.9272	.3746	2.4751	2.6695
23	.3907	.9205	.4245	1.0864	69	.9336	.3584	2.6051	2.7904
24	.4067	.9135	.4452	1.0946	70	.9397	.3420	2.7475	2.9238
25	.4226	.9063	.4663	1.1034	71	.9455	.3256	2.9042	3.0715
26	.4384	.8988	.4877	1.1126	72	.9511	.3090	3.0777	3.2361
27	.4540	.8910	.5095	1.1223	73	.9563	.2924	3.2709	3.4203
28	.4695	.8829	.5317	1.1326	74	.9613	.2756	3.4874	3.6279
29	.4848	.8746	.5543	1.1433	75	.9659	.2588	3.7321	3.8637
30	.5000	.8660	.5774	1.1547	76	.9703	.2419	4.0108	4.1336
31	.5150	.8572	.6009	1.1666	77	.9744	.2250	4.3315	4.4454
32	.5299	.8480	.6249	1.1792	78	.9781	.2079	4.7046	4.8097
33	.5446	.8387	.6494	1.1924	79	.9816	.1908	5.1446	5.2408
34	.5592	.8290	.6745	1.2062	80	.9848	.1736	5.6713	5.7588
35	.5736	.8192	.7002	1.2208	81	.9877	.1564	6.3138	6.3924
36	.5878	.8090	.7265	1.2361	82	.9903	.1392	7.1154	7.1853
37	.6018	.7986	.7536	1.2521	83	.9925	.12187	8.1443	8.2055
38	.6157	.7880	.7813	1.2690	84	.9945	.10453	9.5144	9.5668
39	.6293	.7771	.8098	1.2867	85	.9962	.08716	11.4301	11.474
40	.6428	.7660	.8391	1.3054	86	.9976	.06976	14.3007	14.335
41	.6561	.7547	.8693	1.3250	87	.9986	.05234	19.0811	19.107
42	.6691	.7431	.9004	1.3456	88	.9994	.03490	28.6363	28.654
43	.6820	.7314	.9325	1.3673	89	.9998	.01745	57.2900	57.299
44	.6947	.7193	.9657	1.3902	90	1.0000	Inf.	Inf.	Inf.
45	.7071	.7071	1.0000	1.4142					

MATHEMATICAL TABLES

Tables 10, 11 and 12 are for convenient reference and will be found useful in numerous calculations.

Table 10. Area of Circles

Diameter	Area	Diameter	Area	Diameter	Area	Diameter	Area
⅛	0.0123	10	78.54	30	706.86	65	3318.3
¼	0.0491	10½	86.59	31	754.76	66	3421.2
⅜	0.1104	11	95.03	32	804.24	67	3525.6
½	0.1963	11½	103.86	33	855.30	68	3631.6
⅝	0.3068	12	113.09	34	907.92	69	3739.2
¾	0.4418	12½	122.71	35	962.11	70	3848.4
⅞	0.6013	13	132.73	36	1017.8	71	3959.2
1	0.7854	13½	143.13	37	1075.2	72	4071.5
1⅛	0.9940	14	153.93	38	1134.1	73	4185.4
1¼	1.227	14½	165.13	39	1194.5	74	4300.8
1⅜	1.484	15	176.71	40	1256.6	75	4417.8
1½	1.767	15½	188.69	41	1320.2	76	4536.4
1⅝	2.073	16	201.06	42	1385.4	77	4656.6
1¾	2.405	16½	213.82	43	1452.2	78	4778.3
1⅞	2.761	17	226.98	44	1520.5	79	4901.6
2	3.141	17½	240.52	45	1590.4	80	5026.5
2¼	3.976	18	254.46	46	1661.9	81	5153.0
2½	4.908	18½	268.80	47	1734.9	82	5281.0
2¾	5.939	19	283.52	48	1809.5	83	5410.6
3	7.068	19½	298.6	49	1885.7	84	5541.7
3¼	8.295	20	314.16	50	1963.5	85	5674.5
3½	9.621	20½	330.06	51	2042.8	86	5808.8
3¾	11.044	21	346.36	52	2123.7	87	5944.6
4	12.566	21½	363.05	53	2206.1	88	6082.1
4½	15.904	22	380.13	54	2290.2	89	6221.1
5	19.635	22½	397.60	55	2375.8	90	6361.7
5½	23.758	23	415.47	56	2463.0	91	6503.9
6	28.274	23½	433.73	57	2551.7	92	6647.6
6½	33.183	24	452.39	58	2642.0	93	6792.9
7	38.484	24½	471.43	59	2733.9	94	6939.8
7½	44.178	25	490.87	60	2827.4	95	7088.2
8	50.265	26	530.93	61	2922.4	96	7238.2
8½	56.745	27	572.55	62	3019.0	97	7389.8
9	63.617	28	615.75	63	3117.2	98	7542.9
9½	70.882	29	660.52	64	3216.9	99	7697.7

Table 11.   Circumference of Circles

Diameter	Circumference	Diameter	Circumference	Diameter	Circumference	Diameter	Circumference
1/8	.3927	10	31.41	30	94.24	65	204.2
1/4	.7854	10½	32.98	31	97.38	66	207.3
3/8	1.178	11	34.55	32	100.5	67	210.4
1/2	1.570	11½	36.12	33	103.6	68	213.6
5/8	1.963	12	37.69	34	106.8	69	216.7
3/4	2.356	12½	39.27	35	109.9	70	219.9
7/8	2.748	13	40.84	36	113.0	71	223.0
1	3.141	13½	42.41	37	116.2	72	226.1
1⅛	3.534	14	43.98	38	119.3	73	229.3
1¼	3.927	14½	45.55	39	122.5	74	232.4
1⅜	4.319	15	47.12	40	125.6	75	235.6
1½	4.712	15½	48.69	41	128.8	76	238.7
1⅝	5.105	16	50.26	42	131.9	77	241.9
1¾	5.497	16½	51.83	43	135.0	78	245.0
1⅞	5.890	17	53.40	44	138.2	79	248.1
2	6.283	17½	54.97	45	141.3	80	251.3
2¼	7.068	18	56.54	46	144.5	81	254.4
2½	7.854	18½	58.11	47	147.6	82	257.6
2¾	8.639	19	59.69	48	150.7	83	260.7
3	9.424	19½	61.26	49	153.9	84	263.8
3¼	10.21	20	62.83	50	157.0	85	267.0
3½	10.99	20½	64.40	51	160.2	86	270.1
3¾	11.78	21	65.97	52	163.3	87	273.3
4	12.56	21½	67.54	53	166.5	88	276.4
4½	14.13	22	69.11	54	169.6	89	279.6
5	15.70	22½	70.68	55	172.7	90	282.7
5½	17.27	23	72.25	56	175.9	91	285.8
6	18.84	23½	73.82	57	179.0	92	289.0
6½	20.42	24	75.39	58	182.2	93	292.1
7	21.99	24½	76.96	59	185.3	94	295.3
7½	23.56	25	78.54	60	188.4	95	298.4
8	25.13	26	81.68	61	191.6	96	301.5
8½	26.70	27	84.82	62	194.7	97	304.7
9	28.27	28	87.96	63	197.9	98	307.8
9½	29.84	29	91.10	64	201.0	99	311.0

Table 12.   Logarithms of Numbers

No.	0	1	2	3	4	5	6	7	8	9	Diff.
10	00000	00432	00860	01284	01703	02119	02531	02938	03342	03743	415
11	04139	04532	04922	05308	05690	06070	06446	06819	07188	07555	379
12	07918	08279	08636	08991	09342	09691	10037	10380	10721	11059	344
13	11394	11727	12057	12385	12710	13033	13354	13672	13988	14301	323
14	14613	14922	15229	15534	15836	16137	16435	16732	17026	17319	298
15	17609	17898	18184	18469	18752	19033	19312	19590	19866	20140	281
16	20412	20683	20952	21219	21484	21748	22011	22272	22531	22789	264
17	23045	23300	23553	23805	24055	24304	24551	24797	25042	25285	249
18	25527	25768	26007	26245	26482	26717	26951	27184	27416	27646	234
19	27875	28103	28330	28556	28780	29003	29226	29447	29667	29885	222
20	30103	30320	30535	30750	30963	31175	31387	31597	31806	32015	212
21	32222	32428	32634	32838	33041	33244	33445	33646	33846	34044	202
22	34242	34438	34635	34830	35025	35218	35411	35603	35793	35984	193
23	36173	36361	36549	36736	36922	37107	37291	37475	37658	37840	185
24	38021	38202	38382	38561	38739	38917	39094	39270	39445	39620	177
25	39794	39967	40140	40312	40483	40654	40824	40993	41162	41330	170
26	41497	41664	41830	41996	42160	42325	42488	42651	42813	42975	164
27	43136	43297	43457	43616	43775	43933	44091	44248	44404	44560	158
28	44716	44871	45025	45179	45332	45484	45637	45788	45939	46090	153
29	46240	46389	46538	46687	46835	46982	47129	47276	47422	47567	148
30	47712	47857	48001	48144	48287	48430	48572	48714	48855	48996	143
31	49136	49276	49415	49554	49693	49831	49969	50160	50243	50379	138
32	50515	50651	50786	50920	51055	51189	51322	51455	51587	51720	134
33	51851	51983	52114	52244	52375	52504	52634	52763	52892	53020	130
34	53148	53275	53403	53529	53656	53782	53908	54033	54158	54283	126
35	54407	54531	54654	54777	54900	55023	55145	55267	55388	55509	122
36	55630	55751	55871	55991	56110	56229	56348	56467	56585	56703	119
37	56820	56937	57054	57171	57287	57403	57519	57634	57749	57864	116
38	57978	58093	58206	58320	58433	58546	58659	58771	58883	58995	113
39	59106	59218	59329	59439	59550	59660	59770	59879	59988	60097	110
40	60206	60314	60423	60531	60638	60746	60853	60959	61066	61172	107
41	61278	61384	61490	61595	61700	61805	61909	62014	62118	62221	104
42	62325	62428	62531	62634	62737	62839	62941	63043	63144	63246	102
43	63347	63448	63548	63649	63749	63849	63949	64048	64147	64246	99
44	64345	64444	64542	64640	64738	64836	64933	65031	65128	65225	98
45	65321	65418	65514	65610	65706	65801	65896	65992	66087	66181	96
46	66276	66370	66464	66558	66652	66745	66839	66932	67025	67117	95
47	67210	67302	67394	67486	67578	67669	67761	67852	67943	68034	92
48	68124	68215	68305	68395	68485	68574	68664	68753	68842	68931	90
49	69020	69108	69197	69285	69373	69461	69548	69636	69723	69810	88
50	69897	69984	70070	70157	70243	70329	70415	70501	70586	70672	86
51	70757	70842	70927	71012	71096	71181	71265	71349	71433	71517	84
52	71600	71684	71767	71850	71933	72016	72099	72181	72263	72346	82
53	72428	72509	72591	72673	72754	72835	72916	72997	73078	73159	81
54	73239	73320	73400	73480	73560	73640	73719	73799	73878	73957	80

Table 12. Logarithms of Numbers (Cont'd)

No.	0	1	2	3	4	5	6	7	8	9	Diff.
55	74036	74115	74194	74273	74351	74429	74507	74586	74663	74741	78
56	74819	74896	74974	75051	75128	75205	75282	75358	75435	75511	77
57	75587	75664	75740	75815	75891	75967	76042	76118	76193	76268	75
58	76343	76418	76492	76567	76641	76716	76790	76864	76938	77012	74
59	77085	77159	77232	77305	77379	77452	77525	77597	77670	77743	73
60	77815	77887	77960	78032	78104	78176	78247	78319	78390	78462	72
61	78533	78604	78675	78746	78817	78888	78958	79029	79099	79169	71
62	79239	79309	79379	79449	79518	79588	79657	79727	79796	79865	70
63	79934	80003	80072	80140	80209	80277	80346	80414	80482	80550	69
64	80618	80686	80754	80821	80889	80956	81023	81090	81158	81224	68
65	81291	81358	81425	81491	81558	81624	81690	81757	81823	81889	67
66	81954	82020	82086	82151	82217	82282	82347	82413	82478	82543	66
67	82607	82672	82737	82802	82866	82930	82995	83059	83123	83187	64
68	83251	83315	83378	83442	83506	83569	83632	83696	83759	83822	63
69	83885	83948	84011	84073	84136	84198	84261	84323	84386	84448	63
70	84510	84572	84634	84696	84757	84819	84880	84942	85003	85065	62
71	85126	85187	85248	85309	85370	85431	85491	85552	85612	85673	61
72	85733	85794	85854	85914	85974	86034	86094	86153	86213	86273	60
73	86332	86392	86451	86510	86570	86629	86688	86747	86806	86864	59
74	86923	86982	87040	87099	87157	87216	87274	87332	87390	87448	58
75	87506	87564	87622	87680	87737	87795	87852	87910	87967	88024	57
76	88081	88138	88196	88252	88309	88366	88423	88480	88536	88593	57
77	88649	88705	88762	88818	88874	88930	88986	89042	89098	89154	56
78	89209	89265	89321	89376	89432	89487	89542	89597	89653	89708	55
79	89763	89818	89873	89927	89982	90037	90091	90146	90200	90255	54
80	90309	90363	90417	90472	90526	90580	90634	90687	90741	90795	54
81	90849	90902	90956	91009	91062	91116	91169	91222	91275	91328	53
82	91381	91434	91487	91540	91593	91645	91698	91751	91803	91855	53
83	91908	91960	92012	92065	92117	92169	92221	92273	92324	92376	52
84	92428	92480	92531	92583	92634	92686	92737	92788	92840	92891	51
85	92942	92993	93044	93095	93146	93197	93247	93298	93349	93399	51
86	93450	93500	93551	93601	93651	93702	93752	93802	93852	93902	50
87	93952	94002	94052	94101	94151	94201	94250	94300	94349	94399	49
88	94448	94498	94547	94596	94645	94694	94743	94792	94841	94890	49
89	94939	94988	95036	95085	95134	95182	95231	95279	95328	95376	48
90	95424	95472	95521	95569	95617	95665	95713	95761	95809	95856	48
91	95904	95952	95999	96047	96095	96142	96190	96237	96284	96332	48
92	96379	96426	96473	96520	96567	96614	96661	96708	96755	96802	47
93	96848	96895	96942	96988	97035	97081	97128	97174	97220	97267	47
94	97313	97359	97405	97451	97497	97543	97589	97635	97681	97727	46
95	97772	97818	97864	97909	97955	98000	98046	98091	98137	98182	46
96	98227	98272	98318	98363	98408	98453	98498	98543	98588	98632	45
97	98677	98722	98767	98811	98856	98900	98945	98989	99034	99078	45
98	99123	99167	99211	99255	99300	99344	99388	99432	99476	99520	44
99	99564	99607	99651	99695	99739	99782	99826	99870	99913	99957	44

SUMMARY

This chapter has pointed out the need for mathematics in the plumbing trade. A brief description has been given in addition, subtraction, multiplication, division, and fractions. This chapter has also explained the powers of numbers, the square root, cube root, and the process of measuring objects that occupy space.

Mathematics is very important in designing and planning a plumbing system. The piping system must be so designed to give maximum efficiency through proper installation. This is accomplished by using the proper size (diameter) pipe, length of pipe cut to a minimum, and as few turns as possible. This can only be accomplished through the use of mathematics in calculating the proper designed system, pipe, and fixtures.

REVIEW QUESTIONS

1. How would you find the volume of a cone?

2. What symbol is used to mean the ratio of the circumference of a circle to its diameter?

3. What is the definition of an abstract number?

4. What is the definition of a concrete number?

5. How many sides are in a heptagon; nonagon; decagon; and a pentagon?

CHAPTER 2

Physics for Plumbers & Pipe Fitters

By definition, physics is *the science or group of sciences that treats of the phenomena associated with matter in general, especially in its relations to energy, and of the laws governing these phenomena, excluding the special laws and phenomena peculiar to living matter (biology) or to special kinds of matter (chemistry).* Physics is generally considered to treat of:

1. The constitution and properties of matter.
2. Mechanics.
3. Acoustics.
4. Heat.
5. Optics.
6. Electricity and magnetism.

As sometimes used in a limited sense, physics embraces only the last four divisions; more generally it includes all the physical sciences.

According to Barker, physics regards matter solely as the vehicle of energy. From this point of view, physics may be defined as *that department of science whose province it is to investigate all those phenomena of nature which depend either upon the transference of energy from one portion of matter to another, or upon its transformation into any of the forms which it is capable of assuming.* In a word, physics may be regarded as the science of energy, precisely as chemistry may be regarded as the science of matter.

The scope of physics extends considerably beyond that which is of importance to the plumber in the performance of his work. Only such subjects as will be of use to him will be presented here. In this connection, he should thoroughly study this chapter, and should not be satisfied with simply an understanding of why pipes burst in freezing weather or why water circulates in hot-water heating systems, but should know the reasons for all the various phenomena commonly observed by him in his work. For instance, he should know why pipes become air bound; why air chambers on pumps fill with water; why a boiler water gauge does not register the true water level; why a bucket-valve pump delivers more than its displacement, etc. The importance of some of the matter given may not be apparent to the student; however, it is essential to the workman in the intelligent performance of his work.

MEASUREMENTS

Physics begins with measurements, according to Plato, and in fact, if arithmetic, mensuration, and weighing are taken away from any art, that which remains will not be much.

There are three fundamental kinds of measurements:

1. Length.
2. Mass.
3. Time.

In addition to these, there are *derived* measurements of:

1. Area.
2. Volume.

These are called *derived* because they are the products of two and three lengths respectively. Various units are used for these measurements. The plumber uses the ordinary unit such as inches, pounds, and seconds for fundamental measurements, and square inches and cubic inches for the derived measurements. In addition

Fig. 1. A Stanley two-foot four-fold boxwood rule.

to measuring the size or weight of an object, other kinds of measurement are necessary in physics, such as the measurement of pressure, temperature, etc. Such measurements are indicated by instruments provided with arbitrary scales divided into standard divisions, each division standing for a unit of pressure, temperature, etc.

Measuring Devices

For ordinary linear measurements, such as measuring pipe lengths, the familiar carpenter's six-foot folding rule is commonly used. Owing to the rough usage given to plumbers' tools, easily broken rules should be avoided. A strong brass-bound rule, such as shown in Fig. 1, is often used. The drafting scales on this rule are ordinarily not necessary, though occasion may arise for their use in scaling any measurement that may be omitted on a drawing or blueprint. An even more desirable form of the *two-foot rule* is the caliper rule shown in Fig. 2, which permits the more convenient and precise measurement of pipe diameters, thickness of cast plates, etc.

Most commonly used for measurement are the wood folding rule (Fig. 3) and the steel cased rule. The steel cased measuring

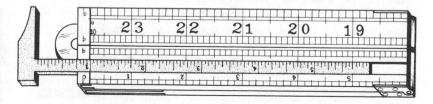

Fig. 2. A Lufkin two-foot four-fold boxwood rule.

61

rule (Fig. 4) is enclosed, as the name implies, in a metal case with the measuring tape folding into the device for ease of carrying and use. Both the folding and tape rule are usually six feet

Fig. 3. A common six-foot folding rule.

long, although many of the steel tapes are available in eight- and ten-foot lengths, making floor-to-ceiling measurements much easier.

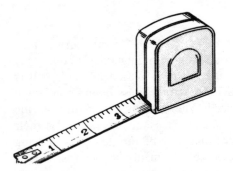

Fig. 4. Cased steel measuring tape.

A rule used extensively is the spring-joint multifold extension rule shown in Fig. 5. Such measuring devices as just described usually answer the needs of the plumber. However, it is occasionally necessary to take small measurements for packing thicknesses and for the thickness of sheet metal, aluminum, brass, etc. The measuring instrument used for this purpose is known as a micrometer caliper, a typical one for general use is shown in Fig. 6.

Fig. 5. The Lufkin spring-joint multifold wood rule.

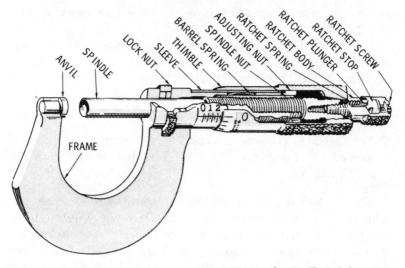

Fig. 6. Phantom view of Starrett micrometer calipers showing construction and method of measuring.

The method of reading a micrometer caliper to ten-thousandths of an inch is explained in Fig. 6. Having found the thickness of metal in decimal fractions of an inch, the corresponding gauge number is found by consulting the proper gauge table.

READING A MICROMETER

The principle of the micrometer consists of a highly accurate ground screw or spindle which is rotated in a fixed nut, thus opening or closing the distance between two measuring faces on the ends of an anvil and spindle. A piece of work is measured by placing it between the anvil and spindle faces and rotating the spindle by means of the thimble until the anvil and spindle both contact the work. The desired work dimensions is then found from the micrometer reading indicated by the graduations on the sleeve and thimble as described in the following paragraphs.

Since the pitch of the screw thread on the spindle is 1/40″, or 40 threads per inch in micrometers graduated to measure in inches, one complete revolution of the thimble advances the spindle face toward or away from the anvil face precisely 1/40 or .025 inch.

The longitudinal line on the sleeve is divided into 40 equal parts by vertical lines that correspond to the number of threads on the spindle. Therefore, each vertical line designates 1/40 or .025 inch, and every fourth line (which is longer than the others) designates hundreds of thousandths.

For example: The line marked "1" represents .100"; the line marked "2" represents .200"; the line marked "3" represents .300", etc.

The beveled edge of the thimble is divided into 25 equal parts with each line representing .001" and every line numbered consecutively. Rotating the thimble from one of these lines to the next moves the spindle longitudinally 1/25 of .025" or .001 inch; rotating two divisions represents .002", etc. Twenty-five divisions indicate a complete revolution (.025 or 1/40 of an inch).

To read the micrometer in thousandths, multiply the number of vertical divisions visible on the sleeve by .025", and to this add the number of thousandths indicated by the line on the thimble which coincides with the longitudinal line on the sleeve.

Example: Refer to the illustration in Fig. 7.

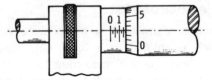

Fig. 7. Reading the micrometer calipers.

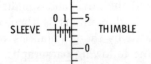

READING .178"

Courtesy The L. S. Starrett Co.

The "1" line on the sleeve is visible, representing .100"
There are 3 additional lines visible,
    each representing .025".   Thus, 3 × .025" = .075"
Line "3" on the thimble coincides with the longi-
    tudinal line on the sleeve, each line
    representing .001".   Thus, 3 × .001" = .003"
The micrometer reading is therefore $\overline{.178"}$

An easy way to remember how to read the micrometer is to think of the various units as if you were making change from a ten-dollar bill. Count the figures on the sleeve as dollars, the vertical lines on the sleeve as quarters, and the divisions on the thimble as cents. Add up your change and put a decimal point instead of a dollar sign in front of the figures.

ADJUSTING OUTSIDE MICROMETER CALIPERS

Although adjustment of a micrometer is rarely needed, they can be readily adjusted as follows:

1. If any play should develop in the spindle screw threads due to wear of the spindle nut after long use, first back off the thimble, insert the spanner wrench in the slot of the adjusting nut and tighten just enough to eliminate the play.
2. After carefully cleaning all dirt or grit from the measuring faces of the anvil and spindle, bring them together and insert the spanner wrench in the small slot of the sleeve. Then turn the sleeve until the line on the sleeve coincides with the zero line on the thimble.

GAUGE STANDARDS

The thickness of sheet metal and diameters of wires are usually indicated by gauge numbers called the *gauge*. Numerous gauges for sheet metal and wire have been in use which leads, in many cases, to confusion. The chief manufacturers, at the suggestion of the Bureau of Standards, agreed that it would be well to designate the American Steel & Wire Co.'s gauge (which is the same as the Washburn & Moen and the Roebling gauge) as the steel-wire gauge to use for steel wires. This gauge is abbreviated S. W. G., or Stl. W. G. when necessary to distinguish it from S. W. G., the abbreviation for the British standard wire gauge.

The American (A. W. G.) or Brown & Sharpe wire gauge is practically the only gauge used for copper and aluminum wire, and for wires in electrical work. An act of Congress on March 3, 1893, legalized a gauge to be used by the custom-house departments for sheet iron and sheet steel, the gauge being known as the U. S. standard sheet-metal gauge. This gauge is used by sheet-metal manufacturers.

Gauge Numbers

The *gauge numbers,* as given in the first column of Table 1, are *retrogressive* for many gauges — that is, a larger gauge number denotes a smaller wire, the number of the wire corresponding approximately to the number of drawings to which it has been subjected. The diameters of the wires of successive numbers increase according to a geometrical ratio. The basic sizes are No. 36 wire, which is .005 in. and No. 0000, which is .460 inch in

Courtesy The L. S. Starrett Co.

Fig. 8. Starrett sheet-metal gauge.

diameter. Between these two sizes are thirty-eight sizes, each succeeding one being derived from the preceding size by multiplying it by the standard ratio, which is 1.1229322. For practical purposes, this ratio may be assumed as 1.123. Hence, the diameter of each succeeding number is found by multiplying the diameter of the preceding number by 1.123.

Gauge Plates

In order to conveniently and quickly measure the thickness of sheet metal or the size of wire, a gauge may be obtained having numbered slots or holes into which the sheet metal or wire may be fitted. These gauges, which are usually circular or rectangular in shape, are shown in Figs. 8 and 9. Obviously, they are time savers as their use avoids setting and reading a micrometer caliper and reference to a gauge table.

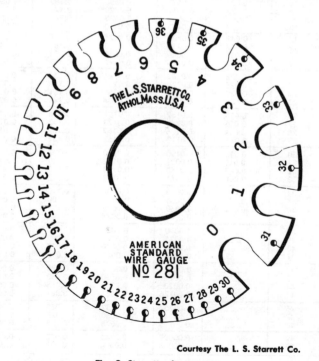

Courtesy The L. S. Starrett Co.

Fig. 9. Starrett wire gauge.

Table 1. Wire Gauge

No. of Wire Gauge	Birmingham or Stub's Iron Wire	American or Brown & Sharpe	Washburn & Moen, American Steel & Wire Co., and Roebling	Stub's Steel Wire	British Imperial Wire
0000000	....	....	0.4900	....	0.5000
000000	....	0.5800	0.4615	....	0.4640
00000	0.500	0.5165	0.4305	....	0.4320
0000	0.454	0.4600	0.3938	....	0.4000
000	0.425	0.4096	0.3625	....	0.3720
00	0.380	0.3648	0.3310	....	0.3480
0	0.340	0.3249	0.3065	....	0.3240
1	0.300	0.2893	0.2830	0.227	0.3000
2	0.284	0.2576	0.2625	0.219	0.2760
3	0.259	0.2294	0.2437	0.212	0.2520
4	0.238	0.2043	0.2253	0.207	0.2320
5	0.220	0.1819	0.2070	0.204	0.2120
6	0.203	0.1620	0.1920	0.201	0.1920
7	0.180	0.1443	0.1770	0.199	0.1760
8	0.165	0.1285	0.1620	0.197	0.1600
9	0.148	0.1144	0.1483	0.194	0.1440
10	0.134	0.1019	0.1350	0.191	0.1280
11	0.120	0.0907	0.1205	0.188	0.1160
12	0.109	0.0808	0.1055	0.185	0.1040
13	0.095	0.0720	0.0915	0.182	0.0920
14	0.083	0.0641	0.0800	0.180	0.0800
15	0.072	0.0571	0.0720	0.178	0.0720
16	0.065	0.0508	0.0625	0.175	0.0640
17	0.058	0.0453	0.0540	0.172	0.0560
18	0.049	0.0403	0.0475	0.168	0.0480
19	0.042	0.0359	0.0410	0.164	0.0400
20	0.035	0.0320	0.0348	0.161	0.0360
21	0.032	0.0285	0.0317	0.157	0.0320
22	0.028	0.0253	0.0286	0.155	0.0280
23	0.025	0.0226	0.0258	0.153	0.0240
24	0.022	0.0201	0.0230	0.151	0.0220
25	0.020	0.0179	0.0204	0.148	0.0200
26	0.018	0.0159	0.0181	0.146	0.0180
27	0.016	0.0142	0.0173	0.143	0.0164
28	0.014	0.0126	0.0162	0.139	0.0148
29	0.013	0.0113	0.0150	0.134	0.0136
30	0.012	0.0100	0.0140	0.127	0.0124
31	0.010	0.0089	0.0132	0.120	0.0116
32	0.009	0.0080	0.0128	0.115	0.0108
33	0.008	0.0071	0.0118	0.112	0.0100
34	0.007	0.0063	0.0104	0.110	0.0092
35	0.005	0.0056	0.0095	0.108	0.0084
36	0.004	0.0050	0.0090	0.106	0.0076
37	....	0.0045	0.0085	0.103	0.0068
38	....	0.0040	0.0080	0.101	0.0060
39	....	0.0035	0.0075	0.099	0.0052
40	....	0.0031	0.0070	0.097	0.0048
41	....	0.0028	0.0066	0.095	0.0044
42	....	0.0025	0.0062	0.092	0.0040
43	....	0.0022	0.0060	0.088	0.0036
44	....	0.0020	0.0058	0.085	0.0032
45	....	0.00176	0.0055	0.081	0.0028
46	....	0.00157	0.0052	0.079	0.0024
47	....	0.00140	0.0050	0.077	0.0020
48	....	0.00124	0.0048	0.075	0.0016
49	....	0.00099	0.0046	0.072	0.0012
50	....	0.00088	0.0044	0.069	0.0010

Courtesy Crucible Steel Co.

MASS AND WEIGHT

These two terms are very frequently confused. By definition, mass is *the quantity of matter contained in a given body,* and weight, *the pull of gravity on the body.* The mass of a given body remains constant, whereas its weight varies according to the location of the body. A given body at or near sea level will weigh more than it will if weighed at the top of a mountain.

The weight of a body not only varies with its distance above sea level, but also with its distance north or south of the equator. Accordingly, some standard for weighing is necessary, the accepted standard being *the pull of the earth on the unit pound weight at or near sea level and at a latitude of 45°.*

The unit of mass is the quantity of matter contained in a certain piece of platinum accepted as the standard unit. Weight is not the correct measure for mass. The correct numerical expression for mass is obtained by dividing its weight as determined by a spring balance by the acceleration *g*, due to gravity at that point. For practical purposes, this means the weight as determined by a good spring balance divided by 32.16.

Example—What is the mass of a sheet of lead weighing 100 lbs.?

$$100 \div 32.16 = 3.11 \text{ lbs. mass}$$

Unfortunately, both weight and mass are by custom expressed in pounds, which is ambiguous and sometimes leads to confusion. The mass of a body is considered in the study of motion.

DENSITY

If equal volumes of different substances such as mercury, lead, iron, wood, or cork are weighed, they will be found to have widely different masses. The term *density* is used in this connection to denote *the mass of unit volume of a substance.*

Thus taking the cu. ft. as unit volume, and the lb. as unit mass, then one cu. ft. of water is found to weigh 62.3 lbs. The density of water and other liquids and gases is not constant but varies

PHYSICS FOR PLUMBERS & PIPE FITTERS

with temperature. Thus, in the case of water, its density at various temperatures shown in Table 2. The density of some well-known substances is given in Table 3.

Table 2. Weight of Water Per Cu. Ft.

Temperature Fahr	32°	39.1°	62°	212°
Weight, lbs.	62.42	62.425	62.36	59.76

Table 3. Densities

Substance	Weight per cu. ft.	Weight per cu. in.	Substance	Weight per cu. ft.	Weight per cu. in.
Aluminum	166.5	0.0963	Lead	709.7	0.4106
Antimony	421.6	0.2439	Mercury at 60°	846.8	0.4911
Bismuth	612.4	0.3544	Nickel	548.7	0.3175
Gold, pure	1200.9	0.6949	Silver	655.1	0.3791
Copper	552.	0.3195	Steel	489.6	0.2834
Iron, cast	450.	0.2604	Tin	458.3	0.2652
Iron, wrought	480.	0.2779	Zinc	436.5	0.2526

SPECIFIC GRAVITY

By definition, the specific gravity of a body is *the ratio between the weight of the body and the weight of an equal volume of water.* Thus:

$$\text{specific gravity} = \frac{\text{weight of body}}{\text{weight of equal volume of water}}$$

Since the density of water varies with temperature, the standard temperature for water has been fixed at 62° Fahr. There are various methods of finding the specific gravity of a substance, depending on the nature of the substance—whether solid, liquid, or gas, heavier or lighter than water, and its shape. The following rule covers all of the various processes for either solids or liquids. The difference arises from the method of finding the weight of the equal volume of water.

Rule—1. Weigh the body.
2. Find the weight of an equal volume of water.

70

3. Divide the weight of the body by the weight of the equal volume of water.

1st method—calculation

Example—A lead keel for a sail boat is 3 × 6 ins. cross section and 8 ft. long. What is its specific gravity?

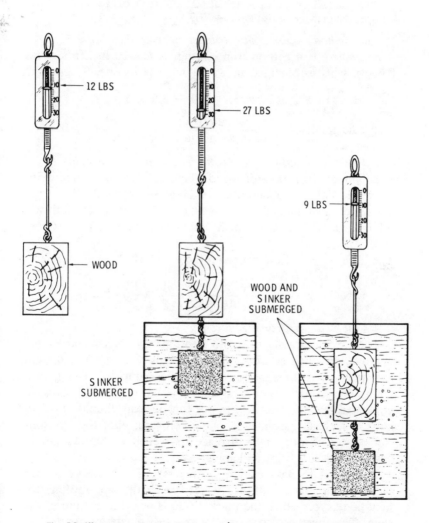

12 LBS

27 LBS

9 LBS

WOOD

WOOD AND
SINKER
SUBMERGED

SINKER
SUBMERGED

Fig. 10. Illustrating the weight of an object in air and submerged in water.

71

First, the keel is weighed and found to weigh 707.9 lbs. By calculation:

$$\text{vol. of keel} = \frac{3 \times 6}{144} \times 8 = 1 \text{ cu. ft.}$$

weight of 1 cu. ft. of water at 62° Fahr. = 62.36 lbs.
specific gravity of the keel = 707.9 ÷ 62.36 = 11.35

2nd method—submersion (object heavier than water)
Example—If a certain iron casting weighs 10 lbs. in air and 8.6 lbs. when submerged in water, what is its specific gravity?

Loss of weight in water = 10 − 8.6 = 1.4 lbs.

$$\text{specific gravity} = \frac{\text{weight in air}}{\text{loss of weight in water}} = \frac{10}{1.4} = 7.14$$

3rd method—submersion (object lighter than water)
Example—If a piece of wood weighs 12 lbs. in air and, with a suitable sinker attached, the combination weighs 27 lbs. when the sinker is submerged under water, and 9 lbs. when both are submerged, what is the specific gravity of the wood? (see Fig. 10).
The lifting effect of the water on the wood is 27 − 9 = 18 lbs.

$$\text{specific gravity} = \frac{\text{weight of wood}}{\text{lifting effect}} = \frac{12}{18} = .667$$

4th method—hydrometer test
The specific gravity of liquid is ordinarily determined by the hydrometer which consists of a glass bulb with graduated stem and weighted with shot to make it float upright. The graduations consist of a paper scale enclosed inside the stem so graduated that the specific gravity can be read directly. In light liquids, such as gasoline, alcohol, kerosene, etc., the hydrometer must sink deeper to displace its weight of liquid than in heavy liquids like brine and acids.

It is usual to have two hydrometers; one for heavy liquids on which the mark 1.000 for water is near the top, and one for light liquids, on which the mark 1.000 is near the bottom of the stem. The most common use of the hydrometer is for testing the specific gravity of the electrolyte in storage batteries as an indication of the amount of charge in the battery.

WATER

This remarkable substance is a *compound of hydrogen and oxygen in the proportion of 2 parts by weight of hydrogen to 16 parts by weight of oxygen*. Since the atom of oxygen is believed to weigh 16 times as much as the atom of hydrogen, the molecule of water is said to contain 2 atoms of hydrogen and 1 atom of oxygen, being represented by the formula H_2O.

Under the influence of temperature and pressure, this substance (H_2O) may exist as:

1. A solid.
2. A liquid.
3. A gas.

As a solid, it is called *ice;* as a liquid, *water*; as a gas, *steam*. Water at its maximum density (39.1° F) will expand as heat is added, and it will also expand slightly as the temperature falls from this point, as illustrated in Fig. 11. Water will freeze at 32° F and boil at 212° F, when the barometer reads 29.921 inches of mercury.

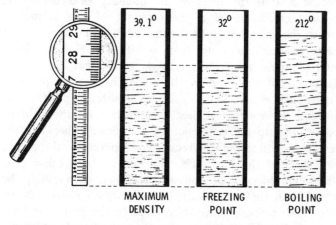

Fig. 11. Illustrating the effect of water at various temperatures.

73

The boiling point of water is not the same in all places. It decreases as the altitude increases; at an altitude of 5,000 ft., water will boil at a temperature of 202° F. An increase of pressure will elevate the boiling point of water. At maximum density, the weight of a cu. ft. of water is generally taken as 62.425 lbs. One U.S. gallon (231 cu. in.) of water weighs 8-1/3 lbs. The figure 8-1/3 is correct when the water is at a temperature of 65° F. The pressure of water varies with the head, and is equal to .43302 lbs. per sq. in. for every foot of (static) head.

HEAT

By definition, heat *is a form of energy known by its effects.* These effects are indicated through touch and feel as well as by the expansion, fusion, combustion, or evaporation of the matter upon which it acts. Temperature is that which indicates how hot or cold a substance is; a measure of *sensible heat.*

Sensible heat is that heat which produces a rise of temperature as distinguished from latent heat. *Latent heat* is that quantity of heat required to change the *state* or condition under which a substance exists without changing its temperature. Thus, a definite quantity of heat must be transferred to ice at 32° to change it into water at the same temperature.

Specific heat is the ratio of the quantity of heat required to raise the temperature of a given weight of any substance one degree to the quantity of heat required to raise the temperature of the same weight of water from 62° to 63° F. When bodies of unequal temperatures are placed near each other, heat leaves the hot body and is absorbed by the colder body until the temperature of each is equal. This is called a transfer of heat.

The rate by which the heat is absorbed by the colder body is proportional to the difference of temperature between the two bodies. The greater the difference of temperature, the greater the rate of flow of the heat. The transfer of heat takes place by radiation, conduction, or convection. Thus, in a boiler, heat is given off from the furnace fire in rays which radiate in straight lines in all directions, being transferred to the crown and sides of the furnace by radiation; it passes through the plates by conduction, and is transferred to the water by convection (that is, by currents).

Bodies expand by the action of heat. For instance, boiler plates are riveted with red-hot rivets in an expanded state; on cooling, the rivets contract and draw the plates together with great force, making a tight joint. An exception to the rule, it should be noted, is water, which contracts as it is heated from the freezing point 32° F, to the point of maximum density at 39.1°; at other temperatures it expands.

HEAT AND WORK

Heat develops *mechanical force* and *motion;* hence, it is *convertible into mechanical work.* Heat is measured by a standard unit called the British unit of heat. The *British thermal unit* is equal to 1/180 of the heat required to raise the temperature of one pound of water from 32° to 212° F. It should be noted that this is the definition adapted in this work for the British thermal unit (Btu), corresponding to the unit used in the Marks and Davis steam tables, which is now the recognized standard.

WORK

By definition, work is *the overcoming of resistance through a certain distance by the expenditure of energy.* Work is measured by a standard unit called the *foot pound.* A foot pound is *the amount of work done in raising one pound one foot,* or in overcoming a pressure of one pound through a distance of one foot. Thus, if a 5-pound weight is raised 10 feet, the work done is $5 \times 10 = 50$ feet pounds.

JOULE'S EXPERIMENT

It was shown by experiments made by Joule (1843-50) that 1 *unit of heat* = 772 *units of work.* This is known as the *mechanical equivalent of heat,* or Joule's equivalent.

Experiments by Prof. Rowland (1880) and others, give higher figures; 778 is generally accepted, but 777.5 is probably more nearly correct, the value 777.52 being used by Marks and Davis in their steam tables. The value 778 is sufficiently accurate for ordinary calculations.

ENERGY

By definition, *energy is stored work;* that is, the ability to do work, or in other words, to move against resistance. A body may possess energy whether it does any work or not, but no work is ever done except by the expenditure of energy. There are two kinds of energy:

1. Potential.
2. Kinetic.

Potential energy is energy due to position, as represented for instance, by a body of water stored in an elevated reservoir, and capable of doing work by means of a water wheel.

Kinetic energy is energy due to momentum; that is, the energy of a moving body.

Conservation of Energy

The doctrine of physics is that energy can be transmitted from one body to another or transformed in its manifestations, but *may neither be created nor destroyed.*

POWER

By definition, power is the *rate* at which work is done; in other words, it is work divided by the *time* in which it is done. The unit of power in general use is the *horsepower,* which is defined as 33,000 foot pounds per minute. One horsepower is required to raise a weight of:

33,000 pounds	1 foot in one minute
3300 pounds	10 feet in one minute
330 pounds	100 feet in one minute
33 pounds	1000 feet in one minute
3.3 pounds	10,000 feet in one minute
1 pound	33,000 feet in one minute, etc.

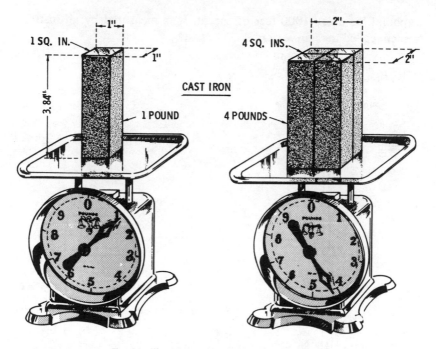

Fig. 12. Illustrating pressure per square inch.

PRESSURE

By definition, pressure is *a force, in the nature of a thrust, distributed over a surface;* in other words, the kind of force with which a body tends to expand, or resist an effort to compress it. Pressure is usually stated in *pounds per square inch,* meaning that a pressure of a given number of pounds is distributed over each square inch of surface. This should be very clearly understood as further explained in Fig. 12.

Atmospheric pressure is the force exerted by the weight of the atmosphere on every point with which it is in contact. At sea level, this pressure is taken at 14.7 pounds per sq. in. for ordinary calculations. We do not feel the atmospheric pressure because air presses the body both externally and internally so that the pressure in different directions balance. Atmospheric pressure varies with the elevation. The pressure decreases approximately one-half pound for every 1000 feet of ascent. It is measured by an instrument called the *barometer*.

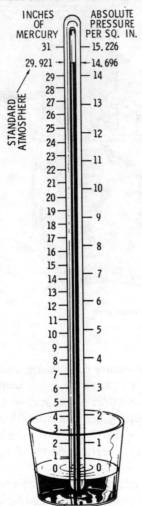

INCHES OF MERCURY — ABSOLUTE PRESSURE PER SQ. IN.

STANDARD ATMOSPHERE

Fig. 13. A barometer illustrating the relation between inches of mercury and absolute pressure in lbs. per sq. in.

BAROMETER

By definition, a barometer is an instrument for measuring the pressure of the atmosphere, as shown in Fig. 13. The instrument consists of a glass tube 33 to 34 inches high, sealed at the top, filled with pure mercury and inverted in an open cup of mercury. A graduated scale on the instrument permits observations of the fluctuations in the height of the mercury column. It is highest when the atmosphere is dry, weighing more then than when saturated with aqueous vapor, which is lighter than air. The height of barometric measurement is about 30 inches.

The column of mercury remains suspended at this height because the weight of a column of mercury 30 inches high is the same as the weight of a like column of air about 50 miles high.

PRESSURE SCALES

The term *vacuum,* strictly speaking, is defined as a *space devoid of matter.* This is equivalent to saying *a space in which the pressure is zero.* According to common usage, it means *any space in which the pressure is less than that of the atmosphere.*

This gives rise to two scales of pressure:

1. Gauge.
2. Absolute.

When the hand of a steam gauge is at zero, the pressure actually existing is 14.74 lbs. (referred to a 30-inch barometer), or that of the atmosphere. The scale in the gauge is not marked at this point (14.74 lbs.), but at zero because, in the steam boiler as well as any other vessel under pressure, the important measurement is the difference of pressure between the inside and outside. This difference of pressure, or the effective pressure for doing work, is called the *gauge pressure,* because it is measured by the gauge on the boiler.

The second pressure scale is known as *absolute pressure* because it gives the actual *pressure above zero.* In all calculations relative to the expansion of steam, the absolute pressure scale must be used. Gauge pressure is expressed as absolute pressure by adding 14.74, or for ordinary calculations, 14.7 lbs. Thus, 80 lbs. gauge pressure $= 80 + 14.74 = 94.74$ lbs. absolute pressure. Absolute pressure is expressed as gauge pressure by subtracting 14.7. Thus 90 lbs. absolute pressure $= 90 - 14.7 = 75.3$ lb. gauge pressure.

79

The pressures below atmospheric pressure are usually expressed in lbs. per sq. in. when making calculations, or "inches of mercury" in practice. Thus, in the engine room, the expression "28 inches of vacuum" would signify an absolute pressure in the condenser of .946 lb. per sq. in. absolute. In other words, the mercury in a mercury column connected to a condenser having a 28-inch vacuum would rise to a height of 28 inches, representing the difference between the pressure of the atmosphere and the pressure in the condenser, or $14.73 - .946 = 13.784$ lbs. referred to a 30-inch barometer.

Pressure in lbs. per sq. in. is obtained by multiplying the barometer reading by .49116. Thus, a 30-inch barometer reading signifies a pressure of $.49116 \times 30 = 14.74$ lbs. per sq. in.

Table 4 gives the pressure of the atmosphere in pounds per square inch for various readings of the barometer.

Table 4. Atmospheric Pressure per square inch

Barometer (ins. of mercury)	Pressure (lbs. per sq. in.)	Barometer (ins. of mercury)	Pressure (lbs. per sq. in.)
28.00	13.75	29.921	14.696
28.25	13.88	30.00	14.74
28.50	14.00	30.25	14.86
28.75	14.12	30.50	14.98
29.00	14.24	30.75	15.10
29.25	14.37	31.00	15.23
29.50	14.49		
29.75	14.61		

Rule—Barometer in inches of mercury $\times$ .49116 = lbs. per sq. in.

Table 4 is based on the standard atmosphere which, by definition, equals 29.921 inches of mercury, which equals 14.696 lbs. per sq. in., or 1 in. of mercury $= 14.696 \div 29.921 = .49116$ lbs. per sq. in.

THERMOMETERS

This term is generally applied to a glass tube terminating in a bulb which is charged with a liquid, usually mercury or colored alcohol. The liquid contracts or expands with changes of temperature, falling or rising in the tube against which is placed a graduated scale. The common scale is Fahrenheit on which zero is the temperature of a mixture of salt and snow, 32° that of melting ice, and 212° that of boiling water. The Celsius and Reaumur scales, from the temperature of melting ice to that of boiling water, have 100 graduations and 80 graduations respectively. The Celsius is usually called the Centigrade thermometer. The latent heat varies with the boiling point—it decreases as the pressure rises.

STEAM

By definition, *steam is the hot invisible vapor given off by water at its boiling point*. The visible white vapor popularly known as steam is not steam, but a collection of fine watery particles formed by the condensation of steam.

Steam is said to be:

1. *Saturated* when its temperature corresponds to its pressure.
2. *Superheated* when its temperature is above that due to its pressure.
3. *Gaseous steam* or *steam gas* when it is highly superheated.
4. *Dry* when it contains no moisture. It may be either saturated or superheated.
5. *Wet* when it contains intermingled mist or spray, its temperature corresponding to its pressure.

Steam exists when there is the proper relation between the temperature of the water and the external pressure. For instance, for a given temperature of the water, there is a certain external pressure above which steam will not form. Steam is produced by heating water until it reaches the *boiling point*. The latent heat of steam is the amount of heat required to change one pound of water into steam at the same temperature.

Thus, if heat is applied to a pound of pure water having a temperature of 212° F, steam will be formed and in a short time all of the water will be evaporated. If the temperature of the steam so formed is taken, the thermometer will register the same as the boiling water, which is 212°. It has been accurately determined by experiment that 970.4° of heat, or heat units, must be applied to a pound of boiling water to change it into steam at the same temperature, and this heat is called the latent heat of steam.

The various states of steam can be seen in the operation of a safety valve by closely observing it when blowing off pressure. For instance, when the safety valve of a boiler furnishing superheated steam blows off, a very interesting phenomena can be observed. Very close to valve the escaping gas is entirely invisible, being superheated at this point. Further away, the outline of the ascending column is seen, the interior being invisible and gradually becoming "foggy." As the vapor ascends, it gradually reduces in temperature, and the steam becomes saturated and super-saturated or wet, reaching the white state a little further away where it is popularly and erroneously known as "steam." Steam is invisible. The reason the so-called wet steam can be seen is because wet steam is a mechanical mixture made up of saturated steam (which is invisible), which holds in suspension a multiplicity of fine water globules formed by condensation. It is the collection of water globules or condensate that is visible.

MECHANICAL POWERS

By definition, the mechanical powers are *mechanical contrivances that enter into the composition or formation of all machines.* They are:

1. The lever.
2. The wheel and axle.
3. The pulley.
4. The inclined plane.
5. The screw.
6. The wedge.

These can, in turn, be reduced to three classes:

1. A solid body turned on an axis.
2. A flexible cord.
3. A hard and smooth inclined surface.

The mechanism of the wheel and axle, and of the pulley, merely combines the principle of *the lever* with the tension of the cords. The properties of the screw depend entirely on those of the lever and the inclined plane; and the case of the wedge is analogous to that of a body sustained between two inclined planes. They all depend for their action upon what is known as the *principle of work,* one of the important principles in mechanics and in the study of machine elements.

The principle of work states that, neglecting frictional or other losses, *the applied force multiplied by the distance through which it moves equals the resistance overcome multiplied by the distance through which it is overcome.* A force acting through a given distance, can be made to overcome a greater force acting as a resistance through a shorter distance. No possible arrangement can be made to overcome a greater force through the same distance. The principle of work may be also stated as follows:

Work put into a machine =
> lost work + work done by the machine

The principle holds true in every case. It applies equally to a simple lever, the most complex mechanism, or to a so-called *perpetual motion* machine. No machine can be made to perform work unless a somewhat greater amount (enough to make up for the losses) is applied by some external agent. In a perpetual motion machine, no such outside force is supposed to be applied, and is therefore against the laws of mechanics.

THE LEVER

The lever consists of an inflexible bar or rod, which is supported at some point, and is freely movable about that point as a center of motion. In the lever, three points are to be considered; the *fulcrum* or point about which the lever turns, the point where the *force* is applied, and the point where the *weight* is applied. There are three varieties of the lever, as shown in Fig. 14. They differ according to where the *fulcrum,* the *weight,* or the *power* is respectively placed between the other two, but the action in every

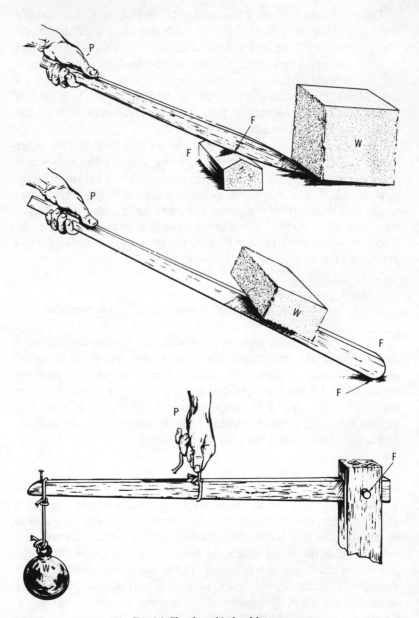

Fig. 14. The three kinds of levers.

case is reducible to the same principle and the same general rule applies to them all.

The following general rule holds for all classes of levers:

Rule—The force P, multiplied by its distance from the *fulcrum,* is equal to the load W multiplied by its distance from the fulcrum. That is:

$$\text{Force} \times \text{distance} = \text{load} \times \text{distance}$$

Example—What force applied at 3 ft. from the fulcrum will balance a weight of 112 lbs. applied at a distance of 6 in. from the fulcrum.

Here, the distances or leverages are 3 feet and 6 inches. The distance must be of the same denomination; hence, reducing ft. to in., $3 \times 12 = 36$ in.

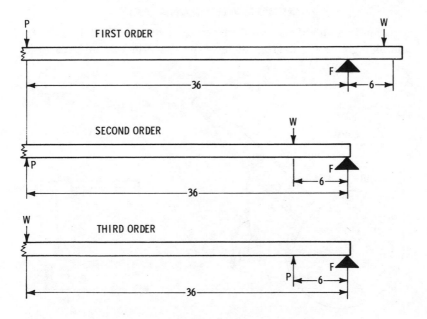

Fig. 15. A diagram of the three orders of levers.

85

Applying the rule:

$$\text{Force} \times 36 = 112 \times 6$$

$$\text{Force} = \frac{112 \times 6}{36} = 18.67 \text{ or } 18\text{-}2/3 \text{ lbs.}$$

This solution holds for all levers illustrated in Fig. 15.

THE WHEEL AND AXLE

This combination is virtually a continuous or revolving lever. It consists of a wheel fixed to an axle or drum so arranged that the operating force is applied to the wheel and the load to the axle, as shown in Fig. 16. Comparison of the wheel and axle with a 1st-order lever shows that, in principle, they are the same.

CHINESE WHEEL AND AXLE

This is a modification of the wheel and axle, and is used for obtaining extreme degrees of leverage. Its principle and construction are shown in Fig. 17.

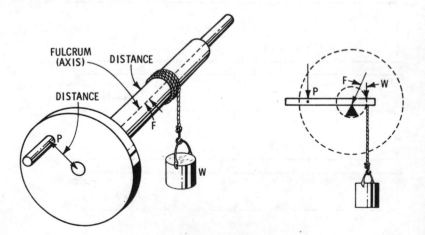

Fig. 16. A wheel and axle compared to a lever.

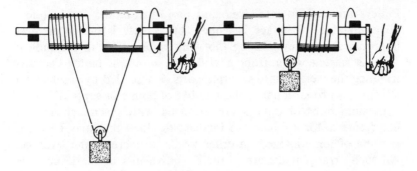

Fig. 17. The Chinese windlass hoist.

THE PULLEY

In its simplest form a pulley consists of a grooved wheel, called a sheave, turning within a frame by means of a cord or rope. It works in contact with the groove in order to transmit the force applied to the rope in another direction, as shown in Fig. 18.

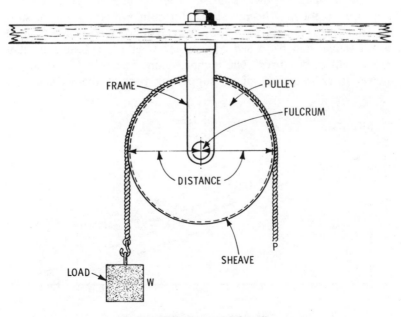

Fig. 18. Illustrating a simple pulley.

87

Pulleys are divided into *fixed* and *movable*. In the fixed pulley, no mechanical advantage is gained, but its use is of the greatest importance in accomplishing the work appropriate to the pulley, such as raising water from a well. The *movable* pulley, by distributing the weights into separate parts, is attended by mechanical advantages proportional to the number of points of support.

Combinations of pulleys are arranged with several sheaves in one frame to form a *block* to increase the load that may be lifted per unit of force applied; in other words, to increase the leverage. All such arrangements are virtually equivalents of the lever. The following rule expresses the relation between the force and load.

Rule—The load capable of being lifted by a combination of pulleys is equal to the force $\times$ the number of ropes supporting the lower or movable block.

THE INCLINED PLANE

This mechanical power consists of an inclined flat surface upon which a weight may be raised, as shown in Fig. 19. By such substitution of a sloping path for a direct upward line of ascent, a given weight can be raised by another weight weighing less than the weight to be raised. The inclined plane becomes a mechanical power in consequence of its supporting part of the weight, and

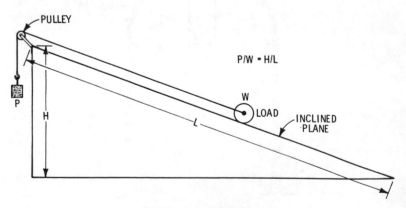

Fig. 19. An inclined plane.

leaving only a part to be supported by the power. Thus, the power has to encounter only a portion of the force of gravity at a time; a portion which is more or less according to how much the plane is elevated. The following rule expresses these relations:

Rule—As the applied force *P* is to the load *W*, so is the height *H* to the length of the plane *W*. That is:

Force:load = height:plane length

Example—What force (P) is necessary to raise a load of 10 lbs. if the height is 2 ft. and the plane is 12 ft.?
Substituting in the equation

$$P : 10 = 2 : 12$$

$$P \times 12 = 2 \times 10$$

$$P = \frac{10 \times 2}{12} = \frac{20}{12} = 1\text{-}2/3 \text{ lbs.}$$

THE SCREW

This is simply an inclined plane wrapped around a cylinder. The evolution of a screw from an inclined plane is shown in Fig. 20. The distance between two consecutive coils, measured from center to center or from upper side to upper side (literally the

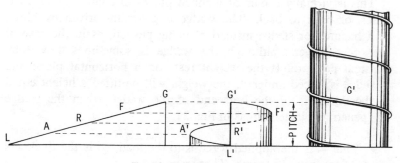

Fig. 20. Evolution of a screw.

height of the inclined plane for one revolution), is the *pitch* of the screw. The screw is generally employed when severe pressure is to be exerted through small distances. A screw in one revolution will descend a distance equal to its pitch, or the distance between two threads. The force applied to the screw will move through (in the same time) the circumference of a circle whose diameter is twice the length of the lever.

Rule—As the applied force is to the load, so is the pitch to the length of the thread per turn. That is:

Applied force:load = pitch:length of thread per turn

Example—If the distance between the threads or pitch is 1/4 in. and a force of 100 lbs. is applied at the circumference of the screw, what weight will be moved by the screw, if the length of the thread per turn of the screw is 10 in.?
Substituting in the equation

$$100 : load = 1/4 : 10$$

$$load \times 1/4 = 10 \times 100$$

$$load = \frac{10 \times 100}{1/4} = 4000 \text{ lbs.}$$

THE WEDGE

This is virtually a pair of inclined planes in contact along their bases, or back to back. The wedge is generally driven by blows of a hammer or sledge instead of being pushed, as in the case of the other powers, although the wedge is sometimes moved by constant pressure. If the weight rests on a horizontal plane and a wedge is forced under it, the weight will be lifted a height equal to the thickness of the butt end of the wedge when the wedge has penetrated its length, as in Fig. 21.

Rule—As the applied force is to the load, so is the thickness of the wedge to its length. That is:

Applied force:load = thickness:length of wedge

Example—What force is necessary to apply to a wedge 20 in. long and 4 in. thick to raise a load of 2000 lbs.?
Substituting in the equation

$$\text{Applied force} : 2000 = 4 : 20$$

$$20 : 4 = 2000 : \text{applied force}$$

$$\text{applied force} \times 20 = 4 \times 2000$$

$$\text{applied force} = \frac{4 \times 2000}{20} = 400 \text{ lbs.}$$

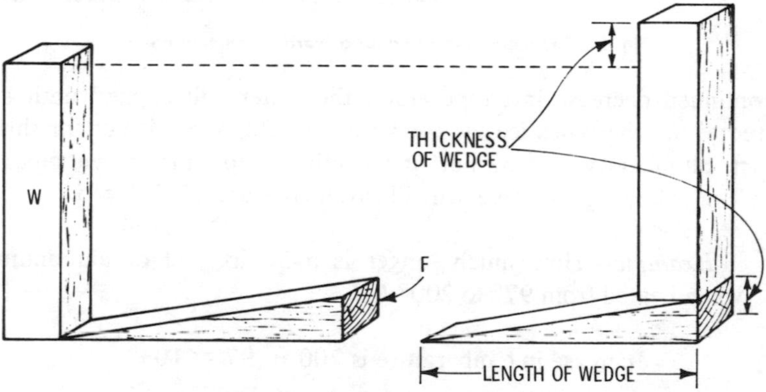

Fig. 21. The application of the wedge in raising a heavy load.

EXPANSION AND CONTRACTION

Practically all substances expand with an increase in temperature and contract with a decrease in temperature. The expansion of solid bodies in a longitudinal direction is known as *linear expansion;* the expansion in volume is called the *volumetric expansion*. A noticeable exception to the general law for expansion is the behavior of water. With a decrease in temperature, water will contract until it reaches its minimum volume, at a temperature of 39.1° F. This is the point of maximum density. With a

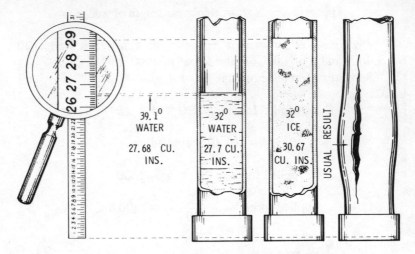

Fig. 22. The expansion of water at various temperatures.

continued decrease in temperature, the water will expand until it freezes and becomes ice, as shown in Fig. 22. Were it not for this fact, plumbers would be out of the job of repairing frozen pipes.

The following example will illustrate the use of Table 5.

Example—How much longer is a 36 in. rod of aluminum when heated from 97° to 200° F.?

Increase in temperature is $200 - 97 = 103°$

Coefficient of expansion for aluminum
from Table 5 = .00001234

Increase in length of rod =
$36 \times .00001234 \times 103 = .0456$ in.

MELTING POINT OF SOLIDS

The temperatures at which a solid substance changes into a liquid is called the melting point. When a solid begins to melt, the temperature remains constant until the whole mass of the

Table 5. Linear Expansion of Common Metals
(Between 32° and 212° F.)

Metal	Linear expansion per unit length per degree F.	Metal	Linear expansion per unit length per degree F.
Aluminum	.00001234	Iron, wrought	.00000648
Antimony	.00000627	Lead	.00001571
Bismuth	00000975	Nickel	.00000695
Brass	.00000957	Steel	.00000636
Bronze	.00000986	Tin	.00001163
Copper	.00000887	Zinc, cast	.00001407
Gold	.00000786	Zinc, rolled	
Iron, cast	.00000556		

Volumetric expansion = 3 × linear expansion.

solid has changed into a liquid. The heat supplied during the period is used to change the substance from the solid to the liquid state and is called the *latent heat of fusion.*

For instance, to melt a pound of ice at 32° F requires 143.57 Btu, or 144 Btu for ordinary calculations. The temperature at which melting takes place varies for different substances.

Table 6. Melting Points of Commercial Metals

Metal	Degrees F.	
Aluminum	1,200	
Antimony	1,150	
Bismuth	500	
Brass	1,700	1,850
Copper	1,940	
Cadmium	610	
Iron, cast	2,300	
Iron, wrought	2,900	
Lead	620	
Mercury	139	
Steel	2,500	
Tin	446	
Zinc, cast	785	

Impure metals usually have a lower melting point than pure metals. Low melting points may be obtained by combining several metals to form alloys. Often an alloy will melt at a much lower temperature than would be expected, considering the melting points of the metals of which it is composed. Those of the lowest melting point contain bismuth, lead, tin, and cadmium.

By varying the percentages of each metal, melting points ranging from 149° to 324° F are obtained; these are only about one-fourth the melting point of the constituent metals. Alloys having such low fusing points are known as *low fusing alloys*. These are considered further in the chapter on Soldering and Lead work.

GRAVITY

By definition, gravity is *the force that attracts bodies, at or near the surface of the earth, toward the center of the earth*. This force varies at different points on the earth's surface. It is strongest at sea level, decreases below sea level in the same ratio that its distance from the center of the earth decreases. Above the surface, the attraction decreases in ratio as the square of the distance from the center of the earth increases. Thus, a body weighs less on top of a high mountain than at sea level.

Falling Bodies

Under the influence of gravity *alone* all bodies fall to the earth with the same acceleration of velocity. *Galileo* proved this by dropping balls of different sizes at the same instant from the top of the leaning tower of Pisa. The spectators saw the balls start together and heard them strike the ground together. Of course, anybody knows that if, for instance, a feather and a piece of lead were released at the same time from an elevated point, the lead would reach the ground first. It is not the difference in weight that retards the feather but the effect of the air on the less dense object. In a vacuum, all bodies fall with the same acceleration of velocity as has been proved by the experiment illustrated in Fig. 23.

Center of Gravity

Briefly, the center of gravity of a body is *that point of the body about which all its parts are balanced, or which being supported, the whole body will remain at rest though acted upon by gravity.*

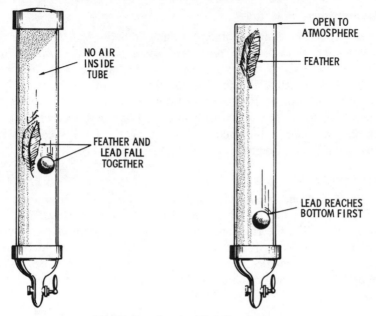

Fig. 23. Experiments with falling bodies.

The center of gravity may be found by calculation and, in some cases, more conveniently by experiments, as in Fig. 24.

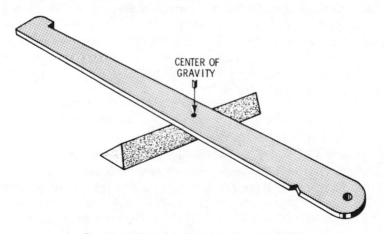

Fig. 24. Method of finding the center of gravity.

Momentum

In popular language, momentum may be defined as *the power of overcoming resistance as possessed by a body by virtue of its motion;* that which makes a moving body hard to stop. Numerically, it is equal to the product of the mass of the body multiplied by its velocity. It is numerically equivalent to the number of pounds of force that will stop a moving body in 1 second, or the number of pounds of force which, acting during 1 second, will give it the given velocity.

Friction

By definition, friction is *that force which acts between two bodies at their surface of contact so as to resist their sliding on each other;* it is the resistance to motion when one body is moved upon another. Were it not for friction, many things would be impossible in mechanics. For instance, power could not be transmitted by belts, automobiles could not be driven through clutches, etc.

Because of friction, bearings must be lubricated, long pipe lines must be oversize to prevent undue loss of pressure, etc. The object of lubricating bearings is to form a film of oil so that the revolving part does not touch the bearing but revolves on a thin film of oil, the friction of solids on fluids being much less than that between solids. Ordinary bearings absorb from 3% to 5% of the applied power; roller bearings, 2%; ball bearings, 1%; spur gears with cast teeth, including bearings, 7%; spur gears with cut teeth, 4%; bevel gears with cast teeth, including bearings, 8%; bevel gears with cut teeth, including bearings, 5%; belting, 2% to 4%; roller chains, 3% to 5%.

HYDRAULICS

The term *hydraulics* is commonly, though ill advisedly, defined as *the science which treats of liquids, especially water, in motion.* Properly speaking, there are two general divisions of the subject:

1. Hydrostatics.
2. Hydrodynamics.

Hydrostatics refers to liquids *at rest,* and hydrodynamics to liquids *in motion.* The outline given relates to water.

Water

Those who have had experience in the design or operation of pumps have found that water is an unyielding substance when confined in pipes and pump passages. This necessitates very substantial construction to withstand the pressure and periodic shocks or water hammer. Water at its maximum density (39.1° F) will expand as heat is added, and it will also expand slightly as the temperature falls from this point.

For ordinary calculations, the weight of 1 cu. ft. of water is taken at 62.4 lbs., which is correct when its temperature is 53° F. At 62° F the weight is 62.355 lbs. The weight of a U.S. gallon of water, or 231 cu. in., is roughly 8-1/3 lbs.

Head and Pressure

These are the two primary considerations in hydraulics. The word *head* signifies *the difference in level of water between two points,* and is usually expressed in feet. Two kinds of head are:

1. Static.
2. Dynamic.

The *static head* is the height from a given point of a column or body of water at rest, considered as causing or measuring pressure. The *dynamic head* is an equivalent or virtual head of water in motion which represents the resultant pressure due to the height of the water from a given point, and the resistance to flow due to friction. Thus, when water is made to flow through pipes or nozzles, there is a loss of head. In ordinary calculations, it is common practice to estimate that every foot head is equal to one-half pound pressure per sq. in., as this allows for ordinary friction in pipes.

The following distinctions with reference to head should be carefully noted.

Total static head = static lift + static head.
Total dynamic head = dynamic lift + dynamic head.

97

Lift

When the barometer reads 30 inches at sea level, the pressure of the atmosphere at that elevation is 14.74 lbs. per sq. in. This pressure will maintain or balance a column of water 34.042 ft. high when the column is completely exhausted of air, and the water is at a temperature of 62° F. The pressure of the atmosphere then *lifts* the water to such a height as will establish equilibrium between the weight of the water and the pressure of the air. Similarly, in pump operation, the receding piston or plunger establishes the vacuum and the pressure of the atmosphere lifts the water from the level of the supply to the level of the pump. Accordingly, lift as related to pump operation may be defined as *the height in feet from the surface of the intake supply to the pump.*

Strictly speaking, lift is the height to which the water is elevated by atmospheric pressure, which in some pumps may be measured by the elevation of the inlet valve, and in others by the elevation of the piston. The practical limit of lift is 20 to 25 ft. Long inlet lines, multiplicity of inlet elbows, and high temperature of the water require shorter lifts. The lift must be reduced as the temperature of the water is increased, because the boiling point of water corresponds to the pressure.

Theoretically, a perfect pump will draw water from a height of 34 ft. when the barometer reads 30 in., but since a perfect vacuum cannot be obtained due to valve leakage, air conditioned in the water, and the vapor of the water itself, the actual height is generally less than 30 feet, and for warm or hot water, considerably less. When the water is warm, the height to which it can be lifted decreases due to the increased pressure of the vapor. For illustration, a boiler feed pump taking water at 153° F could not produce a vacuum greater than 20.78 in. because, at that point, the water would begin to boil and fill the pump chamber with steam. Accordingly, the theoretical lift corresponding would be:

$$34 \times \frac{21.78}{30} = 24.68 \text{ ft., approximately}$$

The result is approximate because no correction has been made for the 34 which represents a 34-foot column of water at 62°; of course, at 153° the length of such a column would be slightly increased. It should be noted that the figure 24.68 ft. is the *approximate* theoretical lift for water at 153°; the *practical* lift would be considerably less. Table 7 shows the theoretical maximum lift for different temperatures, leakage not considered.

Table 7. Theoretical Lift for Various Temperatures

Temp. F.	Absolute pressure of vapor lbs. per sq. in.	Vacuum in inches of mercury	Lift in feet	Temp. F.	Absolute pressure of vapor lbs. per sq. in.	Vacuum in inches of mercury	Lift in feet
102.1	1	27.88	31.6	182.9	8	13.63	15.4
126.3	2	25.85	29.3	188.3	9	11.6	13.0
141.6	3	23.83	27	193.2	10	9.56	10.8
153.1	4	21.78	24.7	197.8	11	7.52	8.5
162.3	5	19.74	22.3	202	12	5.49	6.2
170.1	6	17.70	20	205.9	13	3.45	3.9
176.9	7	15.67	17.7	209.6	14	1.41	1.6

FLOW OF WATER IN PIPES

The quantity of water discharged through a pipe depends on:

1. The *head,* which is the vertical distance between the level surface of still water in the chamber at the entrance end of the pipe and the level of the center of the discharge end of the pipe.
2. The length of the pipe.
3. The character of the interior surface of the pipe as to smoothness.
4. The number and sharpness of the bends, but is independent of the position of the pipe, as horizontal or inclined upward or downward. The head, instead of being an actual distance between levels, may be caused by pressure, as by a pump, in which case the head is calculated as a vertical distance corresponding to the pressure. 1 lb. per sq. in. = 2.309 ft. head, or 1 ft. head = .433 lb. per sq. in.

ELEMENTARY PUMPS

There are three elements necessary for the operation of a pump:

1. Inlet or suction valve.
2. Piston or plunger.
3. Discharge valve.

Simple pumps may be divided into two classes:

1. Lift pumps.
2. Force pumps.

A lift pump is one which does not elevate the water higher than the lift; a force pump operates against both lift and head.

Lift Pumps

Fig. 25 shows the essentials and working principle of a simple lift pump. In this type of pump there are two valves which are known as the *foot valve* and the *bucket valve*. During the up stroke, the bucket valve is closed and the foot valve is open,

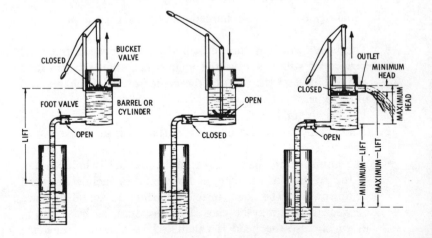

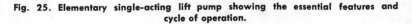

Fig. 25. Elementary single-acting lift pump showing the essential features and cycle of operation.

allowing the atmosphere to force the water into the cylinder. When the piston begins to descend, the foot valve closes and the bucket valve opens, which transfers the water in the cylinder from the lower side of the piston to the upper side.

During the next up stroke, the water already transferred to the upper side of the piston is discharged through the outlet. It will be noted that as the piston begins the up stroke of discharge it is subject to a small maximum head, and at the end of the up stroke to a minimum head. This variable head is so small in comparison to the head against which a force pump works that it is not ordinarily considered.

Force Pumps

The essential feature of a force pump which distinguishes it from a lift pump is that *the cylinder is always closed,* whereas in a lift pump it is *alternately closed and open* when the piston is respectively at the upper and lower ends of its stroke. In addition to the foot and bucket valves of the lift pump, a head valve is provided.

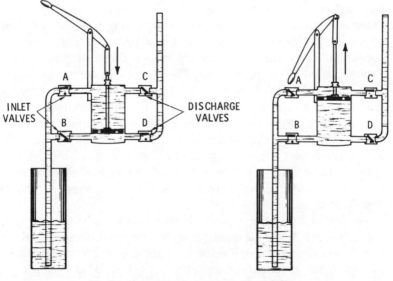

Fig. 26. Elementary double-acting force pump.

In operation, during the up stroke, atmospheric pressure forces water into the cylinder, and during the down stroke this water is transferred from the lower to the upper side of the piston. During the next up stroke the piston forces the water out of the cylinder through the head valve, which closes when the piston reaches the end of the stroke and the cycle is repeated.

A simple form of force pump is one known as a single-acting plunger pump. In operation, during the up stroke, water fills the cylinder, the inlet valve opens, and the outlet valve closes. During the down stroke, the plunger displaces the water in the barrel, forcing it through the discharge valve against the pressure head.

A piston is *shorter* than the stroke, whereas a plunger is *longer* than the stroke. The word plunger is very frequently used erroneously for a piston.

Double-Acting Force Pump

By fitting a set of inlet and outlet valves at each end of a pump cylinder, it is made double-acting; that is, a cylinder full of water is pumped each stroke instead of every other stroke. With this arrangement, the piston can have approximately half the area of the single-acting piston for equal displacement. Accordingly, the maximum stresses brought on the reciprocating parts are reduced approximately one-half, thus permitting lighter and more compact construction. In the double-acting pump there are no bucket valves, a solid piston being used. The essential features and operation are plainly shown in Fig. 26. There are two inlet valves, A and B, and two discharge valves, C and D, the cylinder being closed and provided with a piston. In operation, during the down stroke, water follows the upper face of the piston through valve A. At the same time, the previous charge is forced out of the cylinder through valve D by the lower face of the piston. During these simultaneous operations, valves A and D remain open, and B and C are closed.

During the up stroke, water follows the lower face of the piston through valve B. At the same time, the previous charge is forced out of the cylinder through valve C by the upper face of the piston. During these simultaneous operations, valves B and C remain open, and A and D are closed.

SUMMARY

Physics regards matter solely as the vehicle of energy. This chapter explains why water circulates in a hot-water heating system and why pipes burst in freezing weather.

Included in this chapter are measurements, measuring devices, the use of micrometers, wire and metal gauges, density, specific gravity, and mechanical power. The principals of the pulley, wheel and axle, the inclined plane, and the wedge are discussed along with the expansion of common metals. The melting point of solder and the type of solder used for different metals are discussed.

REVIEW QUESTIONS

1. What are the three fundamental kinds of measurements?

2. What are the two kinds of energy?

3. What is the weight of 1 cu. ft. of water?

/

CHAPTER 3

Plumbing Materials

In his work, the plumber comes in contact with many articles, such as pipes, fittings, and fixtures which are made of various materials, such as lead, iron, brass, etc. These metals are the raw materials from which the articles are made, and the well informed workman should know something about the raw materials. For instance, he should know that lead melts at comparatively low temperatures. If a small blow torch is applied to the lead packing in the spigot joint of a cast-iron drainage pipe, the heat will be carried off so fast from the pipe by conduction that the flame from the blow torch would not even soften the lead.

CAST IRON

Cast iron is defined as iron containing so much carbon that it is not malleable at any temperature. It consists of a mixture and combination of iron and carbon, with other substances in varying proportions. Generally, commercial cast iron has between 3% and 4% of carbon. The carbon may be present as graphite, as in gray cast iron, or in the form of combined carbon, as in white cast iron. In most cases, the carbon is present in both forms. Besides carbon, a combination of silica, sulphur, manganese, and phosphorous are nearly always present.

MALLEABLE IRON

The method of producing malleable iron is to convert the combined carbon of white cast iron into an amorphous uncombined condition by heating the white cast iron to a temperature some-where between 1,380° and 2,000°F. The iron (sometimes called castings) is packed in retorts or annealing pots, together with an oxide of iron (usually hematite ore). The oxygen in the ore absorbs the carbon in the iron, giving the latter a steel-like nature.

An annealing furnace or oven is used for heating, and the castings are kept red hot for several days or several weeks, depending on the pieces. In order for the process to be successful, the iron must have nearly all the carbon in the combined state and must be low in sulfur. Usually, only good charcoal-melted iron that is low in sulfur is used, although a coke-melted iron is suitable, provided the proportion of sulfur is small. The process is not adapted to very large castings because they cool slowly and usually show a considerable proportion of graphite.

WROUGHT IRON

By definition, wrought iron is a slag-bearing malleable iron which contains comparatively little carbon. Much wrought iron now used is made by the puddling process. This process leaves the metal in the condition of a soft plastic ball saturated with slag. This ball is taken from the furnace and dropped into a machine which squeezes out most of the slag. It is then passed through a train of rolls which ejects much of the remaining slag and gives the plastic mass the form of a bar. The presence of slag in the material contributes largely to its fibrous texture, the rolls drawing the metal out into a stringy mass, each fibre of iron being, in fact, the core of a slender thread of slag.

Wrought iron is generally divided into two classes:

1. Charcoal iron, which is made from charcoal pig and usually refined and double refined.
2. Common iron which is made from coke pig.

According to another system, it is classed as:

1. Charcoal iron.
2. Puddle iron.
3. Busheled scrap iron.

STEEL

Steel is an important construction material. Its low price, combined with its great strength, permits its application to the largest and most severely strained constructive members. It can be forged or cast in any convenient form and is readily obtained in form of plates, bars, and other shapes. A disadvantage is that it is rather readily influenced by rust and corrosion, requiring systematic and careful attention in order to preserve it against the action of moisture, oxygen, and carbonic acid.

Upon immersion in a polarizing fluid it is also attacked by galvanic action, in connection with copper or brass. In regard to its percentage of carbon, steel occupies a middle position between cast iron and wrought iron. In common with the former, it has a sufficiently low melting point for casting and, in common with the latter, a sufficient toughness for forging.

According to their varying percentages of carbon, three kinds of steel may be recognized.

1. Soft steel.
2. Medium steel.
3. Hard steel.

Soft steel is nearest to wrought iron in carbon percentage and qualities, being soft, readily forged, and, by careful handling, may also be welded. It is principally used in flanged parts, furnace plates, rivets, and other details which are exposed to alternate heating and cooling or to severe treatment by shaping and forming. Medium steel is harder than soft steel and is used for boiler shells. Cast steel has about the same percentage of carbon as soft or medium steel. In addition, it has silicon and manganese which are needed to produce good castings. Hard steel comes the nearest to cast iron in carbon percentage, and possesses as its most important quality a decided facility for tempering and hardening when cooled quickly in water.

With modern methods, steel is produced by reducing the carbon percentage of cast iron to the desired amount. This may take place in two ways by:

1. Bessemer process.
2. Open-hearth process.

Bessemer Process

This process consists of blowing air into a vertical pear-shaped converter full of molten cast iron. The air is blown in at the bottom, and rising through the molten mass, burns the carbon. If the air admission is arrested at the right time, a steel of predetermined quality and hardness may be obtained. The converter is tripped on trunnions and its contents poured into molds.

The ingots coming from these molds are then rolled into plates or shapes, or forged out as required. Bessemer steel is objected to by some engineers as not possessing a uniformity of quality throughout the material obtained from the same converter. Further, it is not always possible to determine the exact point at which to arrest the admission of air, with some uncertain results.

Open-Hearth Process

In this method, cast iron is deprived of its surplus carbon in a shallow furnace, where the molten material is exposed on a broad surface to currents of air and gases which burn out the carbon. The molten mass can be mixed and stirred, and by removing a small amount as a sample, can also be tested. By this means the reduction of carbon can be more accurately adjusted to the desired degree. The open-hearth product is regarded by many engineers as being more uniform in quality and therefore preferable for most purposes.

COPPER

This is a common metal of a brownish red color, both ductile and malleable and very tenacious. It is one of the best conductors of heat and electricity. It is one of the most useful metals in itself, and also in its various alloys such as brass and bronze. It is one of many metals which occur native. It is also found in various ores, of which the most important are chalcopyrite, chalcocite, cuprite, and malachite. Mixed with tin, it forms bell metal; with a smaller proportion, bronze; and with zinc, it forms brass, pinchbeck, and other alloys.

The strength of copper decreases rapidly with a rise of temperature above 400°F; between 800° and 900°, its strength is reduced about half that at ordinary temperatures. Copper is not easily welded, but may be readily brazed. At near the melting point, it oxidizes (or is burned, as it is called) and loses most of its strength, becoming brittle when cool.

BRASS

This is a yellow alloy composed of copper and zinc in various proportions. In some grades, small amounts of tin or lead are added. Brass is used largely for steam and plumbing fittings, electrical devices, builders' hardware, musical instruments, etc. When zinc is present in small percentages, the color of brass is nearly red; ordinary brass for piping, etc., contains from 30% to 40% zinc. Brass can be readily cast, rolled into sheets, or drawn into tubes, rods, and wire of small diameter. The composition of brass is determined approximately by its color: red contains 5% zinc; bronze, 10%; light orange, 15%; greenish yellow, 20%; yellow, 30%; yellowish white, 60%. The so-called low brasses contain 37% to 45% zinc and are suitable for hot rolling; the high brasses contain from 30% to 40% zinc, being suitable for cold rolling.

LEAD

Lead was the all-important plumbing material a few years ago, but it has since been largely replaced by other metals. Lead may be described as a bluish-gray metal with a bright lustre when melted or newly cut. It is the heaviest of all common metals, weighing .4106 lbs. per cu. in. Commercial lead has a lower specific gravity than pure lead (11.37) because of the impurities contained in it.

The safe working strength of lead is about one-fourth of its elastic limit, or 225 lbs. per sq. in. It is very soft, especially when allowed to cool and solidify slowly. Lead does not crystalize readily. When refined, lead is poured at the correct temperature into a warm mold and allowed to cool. Fern-like crystalline aggregates appear at the surface. In the form of filings, lead becomes

109

a solid mass if subjected to a pressure of 13 tons per sq. in., and liquifies at 2-1/2 times this pressure.

Lead undergoes no change in dry air or in water that is free from air. It becomes pasty at about 617°F and melts at about 650°. It boils at about 1500°C, but cannot be distilled; its co-efficient of linear expansion at ordinary temperatures is .00001571 per 1°F. The strength of lead in both compression and tension is very small. Since lead unites readily with almost all other metals, it is used in many alloys for bearing metals, solders, etc. Alloys composed of lead, bismuth, and tin are noted for their low melting points.

Effects of Acid on Lead

In the use of lead, the following effects of various acids should be noted.

Lime Wash—Lime wash upon lead, after having dried, helps chlorine to form the purple oxide of lead. This shortens the life of lead, and should not be used on the outside of bleaching-powder chambers.

Sulfuric Acid—The purer the lead, the less it will be attacked by pure or nitrous sulfuric acid up to 200°C, the highest temperature employed under normal conditions in concentrating pans. Above 100°C, the action becomes stronger, and at 260°C, the lead is dissolved. Concentrated nitrous sulfuric acid acts at all temperatures more powerfully than pure sulfuric acid, and the effect is greater in the presence of air. Diluted nitrous sulfuric acid of a specific gravity of 1.72-1.76 is not as powerful as the pure acid, although if the dilution is continued beyond this point, the power inmreases again instead of diminishing. A rough surface is more readily corroded by nitrous sulfuric acid than a smooth surface; and the greater the content of nitrogen oxides in the acid, the more the lead is attacked.

Organic Acids—Acetic, tartaric, and citric acids attack lead in contact with air.

Nitric Acid—Nitric acid dissolves lead, forming nitrate of lead. This acid acts very energetically when diluted, but more slowly when concentrated owing to the nitrate of lead being insoluble in strong nitric acid.

Hydrochloric Acid—Hydrochloric acid has practically no action on lead. Boiling concentrated hydrochloric and sulfuric acid at 66°C will slowly dissolve lead.

Aqua Regia—Aqua Regia converts lead into a chloride.

Arsenic and Arsenious Acids—This reacts with lead, yielding arsenate or arsenide of lead.

Peat Acids—Peat acid in water rapidly dissolves lead.

Chlorate of Potash—Chlorate of potash dried upon lead-covered tables will be found to contain traces of lead. Gases of a properly worked sulfuric-acid plant have a very mild action upon the sheet lead of which the chambers are built, and when any severe action takes place, some abnormal condition is sure to have been the cause.

Chlorine—Chlorine does not attack lead to any serious extent; but when chlorine is accompanied by traces of hydrochloric gas, the damage is often extensive.

Lead Poisoning

Lead is a poisonous metal and accordingly, the following precautions should be taken in working with this metal to guard against danger of poisoning.

1. Wash your hands carefully before eating, or before handling tobacco or anything else that will be placed in the mouth.

2. Bathe frequently.

3. Either change your clothing before going to work, or put on outside overalls and jumper while at work. This outside clothing should be washed as frequently as possible.

4. Eat a substantial meal before going to work. With an empty stomach, conditions are more favorable for absorption of lead by the body.

5. Drink water and milk plentifully.

6. If you feel at all sick, consult a doctor at once.

TIN

Tin is a soft metal, the color being white with a tinge of yellow. It has a high lustre, hence is frequently used as reflectors of light. Tin, when nearly pure, has a specific gravity of 7.28 to 7.4, the pure tin being the lightest. It has a low tenacity, but is very malleable and can be rolled or laminated into very thin sheets, known as tin foil. The melting point of tin is 443°F. At 212°F (the boiling point of water) it is ductile and easily drawn into wire. It boils at white heat. It burns with a brilliant white light when raised to a high temperature and exposed to the air. Its specific heat is .0562; latent heat of fusion, 25.65 Btu per lb.

Conductivity is low and it oxidizes slowly in the air at ordinary temperature. When exposed to extreme cold, tin becomes crystalline. Heat conductivity is 14.5, electric conductivity is 12.4 as compared with silver, which is 100. Its weight is 459 lbs. per cu. ft. Tensile strength is 3500 lbs. per sq. in.; crushing load (cast tin) is 15,500 lbs. per sq. in. Due to its high power of resistance to tarnishing by exposure to air and moisture, tin is used as a protective coating for iron and copper. Diluted sulfuric acid has no action on tin when cold, but when tin is boiled in concentrated acid, the metal is dissolved. Coefficient of expansion of tin is .0000151 per 1°F. The principal use of tin by plumbers is for alloying with lead to make solders.

ANTIMONY

Antimony is hard and brittle and resembles tin in its fracture. It crystallizes in the hexagonal system and its color resembles tin more than lead. Specific gravity is between 6.6 and 6.8, and the melting point is 810° to 842°F. Boiling point is between 1090° and 1450°C. Specific heat at ordinary temperatures is .0508. Conductivity for heat (silver being 1000) along the axis of crystallization is 215, and at right angles to this is 193. Conductivity of electricity at 18.7°C is 4.29 (silver being 100). Antimony

112

is used as a hardening ingredient in lead and tin alloys, such as babbitt and various other so-called antifriction metals.

BISMUTH

This very brittle crystalline metal is of a grayish white color tinged with pink or red. The native metal is generally found in Cornwall, Saxony, Norway, etc.; but bismuth is often found in combination with ores of silver, cobalt, zinc, and lead. Its specific gravity is from 9.6 to 9.8, the melting point is 507°F, and it volatilizes at a white heat. It is a remarkable metal for two properties—its specific gravity decreases under pressure, and it expands on cooling. Bismuth is used in many alloys, including solder.

ZINC

Zinc is a hard bluish-white metal with a crystalline fracture which appears as if it were composed of plates adhering together. Zinc in the form of ingots is called spelter; it is quoted by this name in metal-market reports and in business transactions. It is brittle at ordinary temperatures, between 212° and 300°F. It is ductile and malleable, and at 410°F it again becomes brittle. It melts at 773°, boils at 1900°, and volatilizes at a bright red heat; when it burns, it forms zinc oxide. The tenacity of zinc is 5000 to 6000 lbs. per sq. in., or about 1/10 that of wrought iron. Specific gravity is 7.04, and it weighs .2526 lbs. per cu. in., or 436.5 lbs. per cu. ft. Zinc is easily attacked by mineral acids. When rolled into thin sheets, zinc is used for roofs, duct work, eaves, gutters, leaders, etc. It is also used as a protective coating for steel pipe and fencing.

BABBITT METALS

Babbit is an alloy of tin, antimony, and copper, and was discovered in 1839 by a goldsmith, Isaac Babbitt, of Boston. The United States granted Babbitt $20,000 for the right to use his formula in government work, and the Massachusetts Charitable Mechanics Association awarded him a gold medal in 1841. Babbitt's formula is still the standard with the United States Government and many of the larger manufacturers in the country. Unfortunately, competition and high-priced materials have encouraged adulteration, and the genuine formula is not always followed unless the alloy is subject to chemical analysis.

Babbitt metals cover a wide range of alloys of uncertain composition and are frequently made to meet the price offered, without regard to their wearing qualities or to the work for which they are to be used. There are two ways to make Babbitt metals, one with tin for a base, and the other with lead for a base. Adding tin to lead-base metals improves their appearance, increases their cost, and adds to their wearing qualities.

ALUMINUM

This metal is silvery white in color and is not corroded by atmospheric influences or fresh water. It resists nitric acid, but is decomposed by alkalies in sea water, and by dilute sulfuric acid. It is malleable, ductile, and sonorous, and is also a good conductor of heat and electricity. It is the lightest of all useful metals except magnesium. Its tenacity is about 1/3 that of wrought iron. Aluminum melts at 1215°F and does not volatilize at any temperature produced by the combustion of carbon. Specific heat is .2185, and the specific gravity is 2.67. It weighs .0963 lb. per cu. in., and 166.5 lbs. per cu. ft. Aluminum can be readily electrically welded, but soldering is difficult.

OAKUM

Oakum consists of shredded rope or hemp fiber joined together by moistening it with pine tar. It can be obtained in bales or small packages, either loose or slightly twisted, and is used as a packing material.

ASPHALTUM

The name asphaltum is given to a waterproofing paint made from asphalt. Asphalt is black or dark brown in color, and will melt or burn, leaving little residue. It dissolves in petroleum or turpentine. It is used for coating pipes and other metals exposed to dampness and weather.

PLUMBERS' PORTLAND-CEMENT MORTAR

The Portland cement should be mixed with an equal part of clean sharp sand, and then tempered with clean water into a thick mortar. It is used for many purposes, especially for jointing earthenware pipes. This cement will set when water is added. Ready-mixed cement and sand in bags can be obtained from lumber yards and hardware stores, and is recommended where only a small quantity of mortar is needed.

GLAZING PUTTY

Glazing putty is made by mixing 7 parts of whiting with 3 parts (by weight) of boiled linseed oil. It is used for bedding woodwork around fixtures, for bedding cast-iron sinks, etc. It can be purchased ready mixed in almost any amounts from a 1/4-pound can to a 50-pound pail, as well as in the familiar tube for use with a calking gun.

RED LEAD

On passing an air blast over the surface of molten metallic lead, the metal absorbs oxygen from the air and is converted into *litharge*. This oxide is ground into a fine powder and reheated a second time, when it absorbs more oxygen. When it cools, a bright scarlet or orange powder is formed, which is known as *red lead*. Red lead has a powerful drying action on oil, possesses good covering properties as a paint, and may be mixed with other colors.

It is prepared for use by mixing it with boiled linseed oil just before using. It becomes very hard after setting, and when used on upright pipes, will make tight joints that will be difficult to unscrew. Red lead is also used to bed fixtures, set slabs, etc. It should not be used to joint marble work as the marble will be stained by the oil.

WHITE LEAD

White lead is a mixture of lead carbonate and hydrated oxide, and is used in paints and in cement. The white lead is first ground to a powder and then reground to a paste with 10% of linseed oil. White lead is used by plumbers for the same purposes as red lead.

PLUMBERS' SOIL

Plumbers' soil consists of lamp black mixed with a small amount of glue and water. It is used around parts to be soldered to prevent the adhesion of the solder, except to its proper place, thus giving a neat and finished appearance.

BRICK

Clay bricks expand or shrink, depending on the proportion of silica to alumina contained in the brick, but most fire-clay bricks contain alumina sufficient to show some shrinkage. A straight 9-inch fire brick weighs 7 pounds, a silica brick 6.2 pounds, a magnesia brick 9 pounds, and a chrome brick 10 pounds. A silica brick expands about 1/8 inch per foot when heated to 2500°F.

PIPE COVERINGS OR INSULATORS

According to Kent, asbestos is one of the less effective insulators. It is used to hold together other incombustible substances. Any covering should not be less than one-inch thick. A covering should be kept perfectly dry, since still water conducts heat about eight times better than still air. Some good coverings are rock wool, mineral wool, magnesia, hair felt, fur felt, and spun glass.

TEST OF MATERIALS

The strength of the materials used in construction is best determined by tests. Metals are tested for strength in various ways by taking a sample of a standard shape and subjecting it in testing machines for tension, compression, bending, and shearing stresses. There are various terms used in testing, and the following definitions, as given, should be carefully noted:

Alloy cast irons—Irons which owe their properties chiefly to the presence of an element other than carbon.

Alloy steels—Steels which owe their properties chiefly to the presence of an element other than carbon.

Basic pig iron—Pig iron containing so little silicon and sulfur that it is suited for easy conversion into steel by the basic open-hearth process (restricted to pig iron containing not more than 1% silicon).

Bending stress—In physics, a force acting upon some member of a structure tending to deform it by bending or flexure; the effect of this force causes bending strain on the fibers or molecules of the material of which the part is composed. An instance of pure bending stress is given by pulling on the end of a lever, which tends to deflect it while performing work.

Bessemer pig iron—Iron which contains so little phosphorus and sulfur that it can be used for conversion into steel by the original or acid Bessemer process (restricted to pig iron containing not more than 1/10 of 1% phosphorus).

Bessemer steel—Steel made by the Bessemer process, irrespective of carbon content.

Blister steel—Steel made by carburizing wrought iron by heating it in contact with carbonaceous matter.

Cast iron—Iron containing so much carbon or its equivalent that it is not malleable at any temperaure. The committee recommends drawing the line between cast iron and steel at 2.2% carbon.

Cast steel—The same as crucible steel; obsolete and confusing; the terms *crucible steel* or *tool steel* are to be preferred.

Compression—To press or push the particles of a member closer together; as, for instance, the action of the steam pressure in a boiler on the fire tubes.

Converted steel—The same as blister steel.

Charcoal-hearth cast iron—Cast iron which has had its silicon, and usually its phosphorus, removed in the charcoal hearth, but still contains so much carbon as to be distinctly cast iron.

Crucible steel—Steel made by the crucible process, irrespective of its carbon content.

Deformation—Change of shape; disfigurement, as the elongation of a test piece under tension test.

Factor of safety—The ratio between the breaking load and what is selected as the safe working load. Thus, if the breaking load of a bolt is 60,000 lbs. per sq. in., and the working load is 6000 lbs. per sq. in., then the factor of safety is 60,000 : 6000 = 10.

Force—That which changes or tends to change the state of a body at rest, or which modifies or tends to modify the course of a body in motion, as a pull, pressure, or a push; a force always implies the existence of a simultaneous equal and opposite force called the reaction.

Gray pig iron and gray cast iron—Pig iron and cast iron in the fracture of which the iron itself is nearly or quite concealed by graphite, so that the fracture has the color of graphite.

Load—The total pressure acting on a surface; thus, if an engine piston having an area of 200 square inches is subjected to a steam pressure of 150 lbs. per sq. in., then the load or total pressure on the piston is $200 \times 150 = 30,000$ pounds.

Malleable castings—Castings made from iron which, when first made, is in the condition of cast iron, and is made malleable by subsequent treatment without fusion.

Malleable iron—The same as wrought iron.

Malleable pig iron—An American trade name for the pig iron suitable for converting into malleable castings through the process of melting, treating when molten, casting in a brittle state, and then making malleable without remelting.

Member—A part of a structure, such as a brace, rivet, tube, etc., subject to stresses.

Modulus (or Coefficient) of elasticity—The load per unit of section divided by the elongation or contraction per unit of length. Within the elastic limit, when the deformations are proportional to the stresses, the modulus of elasticity is constant, but beyond the elastic limit it decreases rapidly. In wrought iron and steel there is a well-defined elastic limit, and the modulus within that limit is nearly constant.

Modulus of rupture—A value obtained by experiment upon a rectangular bar supported at the ends and loaded at the middle, substituting results in the formula.

Open-hearth steel—Steel made by the open-hearth process irrespective of its carbon content.

Permanent set—When a metallic piece is stressed beyond its elastic limit, deformation occurs, the piece being either stretched, crushed, bent, or twisted, according to the nature of the strain. This alteration in form is known as permanent set.

Pig iron—Cast iron which has been cast into pigs direct from the blast furnace.

Puddled iron—Wrought iron made by the puddling process.

Puddled steel—Steel made by the puddling process, and necessarily slag bearing.

Refined cast iron—Cast iron which has had most of its silicon removed in the refinery furnace, but still contains so much carbon as to be distinctly cast iron.

Resilience—The property of springing back or recoiling upon removal of a pressure, as with a spring. Without special qualifications, the term is understood to mean the work given out by a spring, or piece strained similarly to a spring, after being strained to the extreme limit within which it may be strained again and again without rupture or receiving permanent set.

Shear—The effect of external forces acting so as to cause adjacent sections of a member to slip past each other. When so acted upon, the member is said to be in shear.

Shear steel—Steel, usually in the form of bars, made from blister steel by shearing it into short lengths, piling, and welding these by rolling or hammering them at a welding heat. If this process of shearing is repeated, the product is called *double-shear steel*.

Steel—Iron which is malleable at least in some one range of temperature and, in addition, is either (1) cast into an initially malleable mass, (2) is capable of hardening greatly by sudden cooling, or (3) is able to be cast and hardened.

Steel castings—Unforged and unrolled castings made of Bessemer, open-hearth, crucible, or any other steel.

Strain—Strain is a name given to the kind of alteration produced by stresses. The distinction between stress and strain is not always observed, there being some confusion among writers as to these definitions.

Stress—1. An internal action or internal force set up between the adjacent molecules of a body when acted upon by forces. 2. The force, or combination of forces, which produces a strain in a body.

Tensile strength—The cohesive power by which a material resists an attempt to pull it apart in the direction of its fibers; this bears no relation to its capacity to resist compression.

Tension—The stress or force by which a member is pulled; when pulled, the member is said to be in tension.

Ultimate strength—The maximum unit stress developed at any time before rupture.

Washed metal—Cast iron from which most of the silicon and phosphor have been removed by the Bell-Krupp process without removing much of the carbon, still containing enough carbon to be cast iron.

White pig iron and white cast iron—Pig iron and cast iron in the fracture of which little or no graphite is visible, and is silvery and white.

Wrought iron—Slag-bearing, malleable iron, which does not harden materially when suddenly cooled.

Yield point—The point at which the stresses and the strains become equal, so that deformation or permanent set occurs. The point at which the stresses equal the elasticity of a test piece.

SUMMARY

A well informed workman should know something about the raw materials used in the plumbing industry. This chapter deals with various metals and the effect of one metal when mixed with another.

Included in this chapter are the methods of producing different materials such as cast iron, malleable iron, wrought iron, steel, copper, brass, lead, and tin. For instance, varying percentages of carbon added to steel will change its strength. Brass is a composition of copper and zinc, and is used in plumbing valves and fittings.

REVIEW QUESTIONS

1. What is oakum and how is it used?

2. How is plumbers' soil used?

3. What is the difference between cast iron and cast steel?

4. What is glazing putty?

5. What is malleable iron?

CHAPTER 4

Sheet Metal

The term *sheet* is applied to material (with the exception of lead) having a thickness less than No. 12 U. S. gauge. The U. S. government limits the thickness of sheets to No. 10 U. S. gauge. Ordinarily, sheet mills do not roll stock thinner than No. 30 gauge. As distinguished from *plate,* the term *sheet* signifies that the manufactured product is made entirely from the material specified. For instance, *sheet lead* means lead in the form of a sheet, whereas *tin plate* (erroneously called *sheet tin*) signifies a sheet of iron or steel coated with tin.

SHEET-METAL GAUGES

The U. S. standard gauge for sheets and plate was legalized by Act of Congress, March 3, 1893, as a standard gauge to be used for sheet iron and steel. This gauge has since been adopted by sheet and tin-plate manufacturers. In addition to the U. S. standard gauge, the American or Brown & Sharpe gauge, the Birmingham gauge, and the standard decimal gauge are also used for iron and steel, as well as for copper and brass. A special gauge is used for tin plate, another for zinc. For the dimensions of these various gauges, see Table 1.

The so-called standard decimal gauge for sheet metal was adopted in 1895 by the American Society of Mechanical Engineers and the American Railway Master Mechanics' Association. In this gauge, the number for each thickness is the number of thousandths of an inch of the thickness of the metal, so that a sheet .016 inch thick is No. 16 in the decimal gauge. Many

123

Table 1. Sheet-Metal and Wire Gauges

No.	United States Steel and Sheet Iron	British Imperial Standard	London	Washburn & Moen or United States Steel Wire	Birming-ham or Stubbs	Brown & Sharpe or American Wire Gauge
0000000	.500	.500	....	....	....	....
000000	.46875	.464	....	....	....	....
00000	.4375	.132	....	....	....	....
0000	.40625	.400	.454	.3938	.454	.460
000	.375	.372	.425	.3625	.425	.40964
00	.34375	.348	.380	.3310	.380	.36480
0	.3125	.324	.340	.3065	.340	.32495
1	.28125	.300	.300	.2830	.300	.28930
2	.265625	.276	.284	.2625	.284	.25763
3	.25	.252	.259	.2437	.259	.22942
4	.234375	.232	.238	.2253	.238	.20431
5	.21875	.212	.220	.2070	.220	.18194
6	.203125	.192	.203	.1920	.203	.16202
7	.1875	.176	.180	.1770	.180	.14428
8	.171875	.160	.165	.1620	.165	.12849
9	.15625	.144	.148	.1483	.148	.11443
10	.140625	.128	.134	.1350	.134	.10189
11	.125	.116	.120	.1205	.120	.09074
12	.109375	.104	.109	.1055	.109	.08081
13	.09375	.092	.095	.0915	.095	.07196
14	.078125	.080	.083	.0800	.083	.06408
15	.0703125	.072	.072	.0720	.072	.05707
16	.0625	.064	.065	.0625	.065	.05082
17	.05625	.056	.058	.0540	.058	.04525
18	.05	.048	.049	.0475	.049	.04030
19	.04375	.040	.040	.0410	.042	.03589
20	.0375	.036	.035	.0348	.035	.03196
21	.034375	.032	.0315	.0317	.032	.02846
22	.03125	.028	.0295	.0286	.028	.025347
23	.0281	.024	.027	.0258	.025	.022571
24	.025	.022	.025	.0230	.022	.0201
25	.021875	.020	.023	.0204	.020	.0179
26	.01875	.018	.0205	.0181	.018	.01594
27	.0171875	.0164	.0187	.0173	.016	.014195
28	.015625	.0148	.0165	.0162	.014	.012641
29	.0140625	.0136	.0155	.0150	.013	.011257
30	.0125	.0124	.0137	.0140	.012	.010025
31	.0109375	.0116	.0122	.0132	.010	.008928
32	.01015625	.0108	.0112	.0128	.009	.00795
33	.009375	.0100	.0102	.0118	.008	.00708
34	.0085937	.0092	.0095	.0104	.007	.0063
35	.0078125	.0084	.009	.0095	.005	.00561
36	.0070312	.0076	.0075	.0090	.004	.005
37	.0066406	.0068	.0065	.0085	....	.00445
38	.00625	.0060	.0057	.0080	....	.003965

manufacturing concerns have discontinued the use of gauge numbers entirely in referring to wire, sheet metal, etc., and give the dimension in decimals of an inch.

HOW SHEET LEAD IS MANUFACTURED

Pure refined pig lead is first melted to the correct temperature and then poured into a molding pan which has been preheated. The heat is maintained in the pan until all dross has been thoroughly skimmed from the lead. This slab of lead is allowed to cool slowly. Lead cooled rapidly has a tendency to crystallize, thereby making the finished product a very poor quality sheet, allowing a far more rapid deterioration from chemical action. Dross in sheet lead causes a roughened surface and sometimes penetrates through the sheet, in which case it is not visible because of the glazed surface. Nevertheless, it leaves the sheet so that chemical action of acids would cause a rapid deterioration.

With this method used, it is possible to produce a perfect sheet of lead. When the lead cools, it solidifies into a solid mass which, in the terms of the lead worker, is called a slab. It weighs about 3 tons and is approximately 4 in. thick, 8 ft. 6 in. long, and 4 ft. wide. It is removed when completely cooled with large tongs and placed on the small rolls that automatically carry the slab up to the sheet rollers which do the work of rolling out the lead, reducing it to the required thickness. Ordinarily, sheet lead is produced in the mill from 2-1/2 lbs. per sq. ft. up to any desired weight.

SHEET TIN

At ordinary temperatures, tin can be beaten and rolled into thin leaves known as sheet tin. It comes in weights of from 1 lb. to 20 lbs. per sq. ft.

TIN PLATE

By definition, *tin plate consists of sheets of iron or steel coated with tin for protection against corrosion,* as distinguished from sheet tin which consists of sheets entirely of tin. Tin plate is produced from steel sheets which range in thickness usually from 16 to 38 Stubbs wire gauge. After the sheets are rolled, they are pickled to remove the scale, washed with water to remove the acid, and then annealed, pickled, washed, and passed through molten tin by means of four to six pairs of rolls immersed in the molten tin.

ROOFING PLATES

In distinction from plates coated only with tin, terne plates are made of soft steel or wrought iron and covered with a mixture of lead and tin. There are two methods employed in coating:

1. The old or original method in which the block plates are dipped by hand into a mixture of tin and lead and allowed to take all the coating possible.

2. This is known as the patent roller process by which the plates are put into a bath of tin and lead and then passed between rolls.

SHEET METAL

Iron and steel may be obtained rolled into thin sheets of various sizes. Sheet steel is made from soft steel containing a low percentage of carbon rolled to thicknesses ranging from No. 10 (.141 in.) to No. 30 (.013 in.) U. S. standard gauge. The sizes of sheets generally carried in stock are 24, 26, 28 and 30 in. wide by 72, 84, 96, and 120 in. long. No. 10 to 16 inclusive are also made in widths 36, 40, 42 and 48 in. by 144 in. long; No. 17 to 24 are made 36 in. wide by 144 in. long.

GALVANIZED SHEET METAL

The term *galvanized* is defined as to *heat with a continuous electric current*. The term is almost universally applied to iron or steel coated with zinc by immersion in a molten bath of that metal, without galvanization. Galvanized sheet metal is protected

126

against corrosion, the zinc being covered with a film of zinc carbonate which protects the metal from further chemical action.

If the galvanizing is poorly done and the coating does not adhere properly, and if any acid from the pickle or any chloride from the flux remains on the iron, corrosion takes place under the zinc coating. The zinc used for galvanizing should contain at least 98% pure zinc.

SHEET BRASS

This is a composition of copper and zinc in varying proportions according to the purpose for which it is intended. Here, such alloys as may be rolled and drawn are considered, and in a general way this may be said to include only alloys containing not less than 60% copper. The malleability and ductility depend upon the amount of copper in the mixture. The ordinary yellow brass, known to the trade as high brass (meaning high in zinc), will vary from 60% copper and 40% zinc up to 75% copper and 25% zinc, according to the physical characteristics.

The important brasses are the following:

Drawing brass, for making articles drawn to shapes with punches and dies in drawing presses.

Spinning brass, for making articles which are spun to shape on chucks.

Lead brass or clock brass, which contains a small percentage of lead in the mixture and is free cutting and drilling, but not suitable for drawing or spinning.

Stamping brass, suitable for making articles cut to shape and left flat or bent to shape, but not drawn or spun.

Brazing brass, made of a mixture which will not fuse at the high heat necessary for hard-solder brazing. It is also an excellent drawing brass.

Low brass is an alloy of copper and zinc, meaning low in zinc content, and the name is not generally applied to any mixture containing less than 80% copper. It is darker in color than high brass, and is also very tough and ductile; may be spun and drawn to almost any desired shape.

BRONZE

There is some confusion in the metal trades as to what is meant by *bronze*. In the early days of the art, the name was only applied to mixtures of copper and tin. The name originally designated a noncorrosive metal dark in color, hard in temper, and of high tensile strength, but practice has sanctioned the use of the name for many metals possessing these characteristics regardless of composition.

Commercial or architectural bronze is the name commonly applied to a mixture of 90 parts copper and 10 parts zinc. When polished, it has a rich gold color and is used where ornamentation must be combined with durability. It is extensively used for interior work, such as fireproofing window sash and doors, grille work, elevator enclosures, signs, and tablets. Gilding metal is an alloy containing more copper than architectural bronze, and varies from 12 to 18 parts copper and 1 part zinc. It closely resembles copper in appearance, but is tougher and stronger; it is very ductile and may be drawn and spun or brazed. It is not extensively used and is generally made to meet some special requirement.

SHEET COPPER

Rolling copper to an exact thickness is difficult. By custom, a variation of not over 1/2 oz, either over or under the specified weight, is permissible. The thickness should be indicated either in terms of weight per sq. ft. in decimals of an inch, or by gauge. If by gauge, care should be taken to state whether Stubbs or B. & S. gauge is used.

TEMPER

Any of the sheet alloys may be obtained in the proper temper for the work if care is taken to indicate what is required. Spinning brass is annealed soft. Drawing brass is given a special drawing anneal and the various degrees of hardness in hard brass depends on how much the metal is reduced in thickness. Quarter hard (one number) is stiffer than soft brass, but can be double seamed without cracking. Half hard (two numbers) is a temper suitable for punching, blanking, and bending. Regular hard (four numbers) is too stiff to work beyond a right-angle bend across the grain of the metal. Spring hard (6 to 8 numbers) is sufficiently elastic to return to its original position after deflection.

SUMMARY

A wide variety of sheet metal is used in plumbing work, including iron, steel, copper, brass, aluminum, and various plated sheet metal.

The term sheet is applied to material having a thickness of less than No. 12 U. S. gauge. Sheets of different metals are rolled in stock sizes and thickness. The length and breadth are almost universally given in inches and the thickness usually by gauge.

The prime factor contributing toward the use of stainless steel is its great strength, resistance to rust, corrosion, and general deterioration. Copper is an excellent conductor of electricity and heat, and is used chiefly in the form of tubing for water and high-pressure liquids. Brass is an alloy of copper and zinc. It is used for pipe fittings and valves.

REVIEW QUESTIONS

1. How is the thickness of sheet metal measured?

2. How is sheet lead manufactured?

3. What is roofing plate?

4. What percentage of zinc is used in galvanizing sheet metal?

5. How is brass manufactured?

CHAPTER 5

Pipe

There are numerous kinds of pipe manufactured to meet the varied conditions of service. They may be classed as:

1. According to the material used:
   a. Wrought iron.
   b. Wrought steel.
   c. Cast iron.
   d. Copper.
   e. Brass.
   f. Lead.
   g. Plastic.
   h. Glass.

2. According to the process of manufacture:
   a. Brazed.
   b. Butt welded.
   c. Lap welded.
   d. Riveted.
   e. Soldered.

3. According to the kind of joint used:
   a. Threaded.
   b. Flanged.
   c. Spigot.
   d. Slip.

4. According to strength:
   a. Standard.

b. Heavy.

c. Extra heavy.

WROUGHT-IRON OR STEEL WELDED PIPE

For conveying steam, gas, air, and water under pressure, wrought-iron and steel pipes are largely used. There is a difference of opinion as to the superiority of the one material over the other, especially in the matter of corrosion. Some think that the cinder which remains in the wrought iron breaks up the continuity of the metal and tends to retard corrosion, while others believe there is little or no difference in the rust resisting qualities of the two materials. Wrought-iron pipe, because of the higher cost of manufacturing, has been largely replaced by steel and in some cases by plastic pipe.

THREADED PIPE JOINTS

In screwed joints having strength and durability, it is necessary to have clean-cut and uniform threads. The threads should be tapered and smooth, cut with the correct taper, thread angle, and diameters. Reasonable manufacturing tolerances are allowed on all of the thread elements to take care of variations in threading. The diameters should be such as to allow sufficient hand engagement and yet allow enough threads for wrench or power make-up.

The thread lengths should be long enough to compensate for pipe strains usually present in the various types of thread joint services. A short thread is satisfactory for joints where little or no pipe strains exist, but longer threads are required where extreme pipe strains are encountered, such as in oil-field casing thread joints.

Thread Assembling

In making up screwed pipe joints, it is very important that the threads in both parts are thoroughly cleaned. Any threads which may have become burred or bent should be straightened or removed and a good grade of lubricant should be applied to the threads. The lubricant reduces the friction, which allows the two parts to be pulled up further, resulting in a more effective pipe joint. Pipe joints should not be screwed together too rapidly, in order to avoid raising the temperature of the two parts to a high degree.

The normal amount of external threads to provide a tight joint for various sizes of pipe is given in Table 1. These dimensions have been established from tests made under practical working conditions. In order to obtain the correct thread length listed in the table, it is necessary to vary the torque or power according to the size, metal, and weight of the material used. For example, it requires considerably less power to make up a screwed joint using a light bronze valve than a high-pressure steel valve.

Leaky Joints

Leaky joints can usually be traced either to faulty threading or an improper lubricant. Frequently, the trouble lies in the thread on the pipe which may have been cut with dull or improperly

Table 1. External Pipe Thread Dimensions

Pipe Size	Min. Reg. for ext. pipe thread
1/8	3/8
1/4	9/16
3/8	5/8
1/2	3/4
3/4	7/8
1	1
1-1/4	1-1/8
1-1/2	1-5/16
2	1-5/8
2-1/2	1-5/8
3	1-11/16
3-1/2	1-11/16
4	1-3/4
5	1-13/16
6	1-15/16
8	2-1/8
10	2-3/8
12	2-9/16
14	2-11/16
16	2-7/8
18	3-3/32
20	3-9/16
24	3-11/16

adjusted threading tools, resulting in wavy, shaved, rough, or chewed threads. Wavy threads are noticeable both to the eye and touch, due to circumferential waves or longitudinal flats of slightly helical form rather than the desired true circular form. Shaved threads appear to have been threaded with two dies, one not matching the other, giving a double-thread appearance at the start of the thread. Rough or chewed threads are noticeably rough and torn. Should the threads have any of these defects, it is possible that leaky joints will result.

WEIGHT OF PIPE

In order to adapt wrought-iron pipe to different pressures, it is regularly made up in three grades of thicknesses known as:

1. Standard.
2. Extra strong (or heavy).
3. Double extra strong (or heavy).

For the three grades, the outside diameters of the listed sizes remain the same, but the thickness is increased by decreasing the

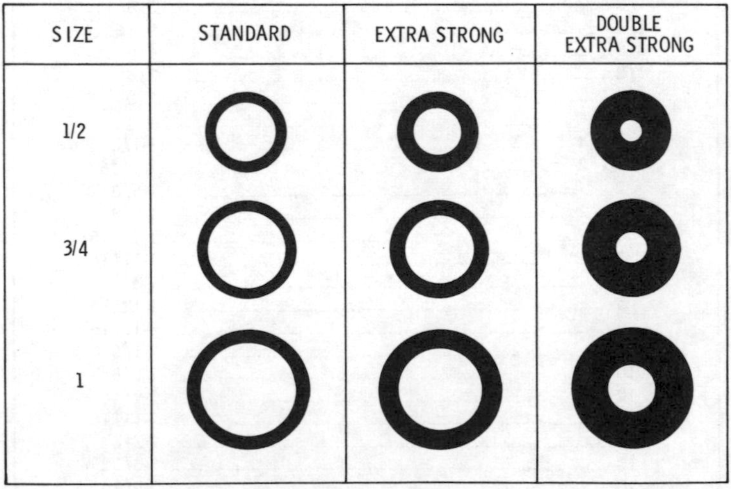

Fig. 1. Illustrating pipe wall thickness which will vary inside diameter.

inside diameter. For instance, Fig. 1 shows sections of the above three grades of pipe of the same listed size.

MANUFACTURE AND TESTS

Welded steel pipe should be made from uniformly good quality soft, weldable steel, rolled from solid ingots. Sufficient crop should be cut from the ends to ensure sound material, and the steel should be given the most approved treatment in heating and rolling. The steel from which the pipe is made must, according to the National Tube Co., exhibit the following physical properties:

> Tensile strength, 50,000 pounds
> Elastic limit over 30,000 pounds
> Elongation in 8 in., 18 per cent
> Reduction in area, 50 per cent

BURSTING AND SAFE WORKING PRESSURES

Numerous factory tests to determine the actual bursting pressure of wrought pipe have proved Barlow's formula to be correct. Barlow's formula:

$$BP = \frac{2T \times TS}{OD}$$

in which,

> BP is the bursting pressure in lbs. per sq. in.,
> T is the thickness of the wall in inches,
> OD is the outside diameter of the pipe in inches,
> TS is the tensile strength.

The value of TS, as determined from actual tests, is 40,000 lbs. per sq. in. for butt-welded pipe, and 50,000 lbs. for lap-welded steel pipe. Table 2 is based on Barlow's formula, and the working pressures given are based on a safety factor of eight.

Table 2. Pipe Test Pressures

STANDARD			EXTRA STRONG			DOUBLE EXTRA STRONG		
Size	Test pressure in pounds		Size	Test pressure in pounds		Size	Test pressure in pounds	
	Butt	Lap		Butt	Lap		Butt	Lap
1/8	700		1/8	700				
1/4	700		1/4	700				
3/8	700		3/8	700				
1/2	700		1/2	700		1/2	700	
3/4	700		3/4	700		3/4	700	
1	700		1	700		1	700	
1 1/4	700	1000	1 1/4	1500		1 1/4	2200	
1 1/2	700	1000	1 1/2	1500	2500	1 1/2	2200	3000
2	700	1000	2	1500	2500	2	2200	3000
2 1/2	800	1000	2 1/2	1500	2000	2 1/2	2200	3000
3	800	1000	3	1500	2000	3		3000
3 1/2		1000	3 1/2		2000	3 1/2		2500
4		1000	4		2000	4		2500
4 1/2		1000	4 1/2		1800	4 1/2		2000
5		1000	5		1800	5		2000
6		1000	6		1800	6		2000
7		1000	7		1500	7		2000
8		800	8		1500	8		2000
8		1000				8		
9		900	9		1500	9		
10		600	10		1200	10		
10		800				10		
10		900				10		
11		800	11		1100	11		
12		600	12		1100	12		
12		800				12		
13		700	13		1000	13		
14		700	14		1000	14		
15		600	15		1000	15		

CAST-IRON PIPE

These are usually made with spigot and bell joints, one end of each pipe being chamfered out to form a socket, bell, or hub, which receives the other extremity of the next length. The head or spigot end is sometimes turned to fit accurately in the bored-out bell, but is usually cast with a raised bead around the end that fits snugly into the socket.

COPPER PIPE

Copper pipe is used extensively in plumbing work, particularly for water lines and radiant panel heating. Its use and method of application and installation is covered in Volume 3 of the *Plumbers and Pipe Fitters Guides.*

BRASS PIPE

The advantage of brass pipe is that it does not rust or corrode, but in cost, it is more expensive than iron pipe. It is made in iron-pipe sizes and is tested to a pressure of 1000 lbs. per sq. in. The temper of the brass is not strictly hard, but just sufficiently annealed to prevent cracking and to make it suitable for steam and plumbing work.

LEAD PIPE

The advantages of lead pipe in plumbing are:

1. Its superior rust-resisting property.
2. Ease with which it can be bent around corners, making fittings and joints unnecessary.

TUBES

In distinction, a tube has relatively thin walls and the listed sizes correspond to the outside diameter; a pipe has relatively thick walls and the listed sizes of wrought pipe do not correspond to the outer diameter. The following properties of a 1-inch tube and 1-inch wrought pipe in Table 3 will clearly illustrate the distinction between tubes and pipes.

Table 3. Properties of 1-Inch Tube and Pipe

	Outside Diameter (Inches)	Inside Diameter (Inches)	Thickness of Metal (Inches)
1-inch tube	1	.81	.095
1-inch wrought pipe	1.315	1.049	.135

PLASTIC PIPING

In recent years, the use of plastic pipe has increased tremendously. Originally it was used primarily for farm water systems and some lawn and golf course underground sprinkling systems. Now, plastic pipe is in use for natural-gas distribution and supply, chemical and food processing, laboratory and industrial waste disposal, industrial and residential plumbing, and for many other applications. Credit for this almost revolutionary development can be attributed to the plumbing industry which devised and developed the new techniques and skills required to make the installation of plastic pipe practical and economical. The plastic piping manufacturers have developed reliable and comprehensive information concerning plastic pipe, recommended methods for joining it, tips on fabrication and installation, and technical data. A summary of plastic pipe information and technical data can be obtained from various pipe manufacturers.

Plastic piping is a unique combination of chemical and physical properties making it available at a fairly reasonable cost. In manufacturing plastic piping products, it is essential that only virgin plastic compounds that meet exacting specifications be used. In following this practice, the special properties of the raw materials will not be changed or diluted. Products in manufacture must be closely tested and inspected to make certain that each meets or exceeds all applicable standards and specifications. If this practice of extra attention and care at the manufacturing plant is followed, the plumber and pipe fitter will know that their field work will be made easier and the completed job will be satisfactory.

The term *plastic* includes a number of materials that differ significantly in their properties, characteristics, and suitability for specific jobs. These differences are important to assist in avoiding misapplications. Plastic materials generally are classified in two basic groups—thermoplastics and thermosetting resins. The thermoplastics can be reformed repeatedly by application of heat. Thermosetting resins, once their shape is fixed and cured, cannot be changed for reuse.

Thermoplastics material is used in the greater portion of the plastic pipe manufactured. A variety of end treatments allows the fabricator a choice of joining pipe to fittings by solvent welding, threading, fusion welding, flanging, or almost any combination of these methods to assure a satisfactory job.

Polyvinyl Chloride (PVC)

PVC has a high tensile strength and a good modulus of elasticity. Therefore, it is stronger and more rigid than most other thermoplastics. The maximum service temperature is 150°F for Type I (Normal Impact), and 140°F for Type II (High Impact). PVC has excellent chemical resistance to a wide range of corrosive fluids, but may be damaged by ketones, aromatics, and some chlorinated hydrocarbons. It has proved to be a good material for process piping (liquids, gases, and slurries), water service, and industrial and laboratory chemical waste drainage. Drain, waste, and vent piping can be joined by solvent welding or fillet welding.

Polyvinyl Dichloride (PVDC)

PVDC is particularly useful for handling corrosive fluids at temperatures 40° to 60° above the limits for other vinyl plastics. Suggested uses include process piping for hot corrosive liquids, hot- and cold-water lines in office buildings and residences, and similar applications above the temperature range of PVC. PVDC pipe should be joined by solvent welding, threading, or as recommended by the pipe manufacturer.

Polypropylene

Polypropylene is the lightest of the thermoplastic piping materials, yet has higher strength and better general chemical resistance than polyethylene, and may be used at temperatures 30° to 50° above the recommended limits of polyethylene. Polypropylene is an excellent material for laboratory and industrial drainage pipe where mixtures of acids and solvents are involved. It has found wide application in the petroleum industry where its resistance to sulfur-bearing compounds is particularly useful in salt-water disposal lines, low-pressure gas-gathering systems, and crude-oil flow piping. It is best joined by *Thermo-seal* fusion welding.

139

Polyvinylidene Fluoride (Kynar)

Kynar is one of the fluorine-containing thermoplastics for piping applications. It is particularly suitable for industrial uses that involve chlorine-containing solutions at temperatures to 250°F.

Polyethylne

Polyethylene is the least expensive of the thermoplastics, and one of the most widely used. Although its mechanical strength is comparatively low, it exhibits very good chemical resistance and is generally satisfactory when used at temperatures below 120°F. Types I and II (low-and-medium-density) are used frequently in chemical laboratory drainage lines, field irrigation, and portable water systems. *Thermo-seal* fusion welding is the best method for joining this material.

Cellulose-Acetate-Butyrate (CAB)

CAB has fairly low mechanical strength and only moderate resistance to temperature, chemicals, and weathering, but is impact resistant. Principal uses have been for carrying salt water, crude oil and natural gas. It should not be used for handling artificial gas or at elevated temperatures. Solvent welding, sleeve fittings, and threading are recommended methods of fabrication.

Acrylonitrile-Butadiene-Styrene (ABS)

ABS has high impact strength, is very tough, and may be used at temperatures up to 180°F. It has a lower chemical resistance and lower design strength than PVC. ABS is used for carrying water for irrigation, gas transmission, drain lines, waste, and vent piping. Solvent welding or threading are recommended fabrication methods.

Crosslinked Polyethylene (CAB-XL)

CAB-XL is a material which has excellent strength characteristics and improved resistance to most chemicals and solvents at elevated temperatures to 203°F. Crosslinking permits high impact strength even at sub-zero temperatures. This material is often suggested for services too severe for ordinary polyethylene. Threading is the accepted joining method.

Glass-Reinforced Epoxy

Glass-reinforced epoxy is probably the best thermoset plastic for piping applications. It has a high strength-to-weight ratio, and has an outstanding resistance to chemicals and weathering.

Plastic-Pipe Connections

A broad range of domestic and industrial thermoplastic and thermoset piping materials are manufactured. Fig. 2 indicates some pressure fittings and pressure valves. Fig. 3 illustrates the threaded fitting. Fig. 4 shows the reinforced epoxy fittings, Fig. 5 *Cabot Thermo-seal* drainage fittings of polyethylene and polypro-

UNION   90° ELBOW

Fig. 2. Plastic pressure fittings.

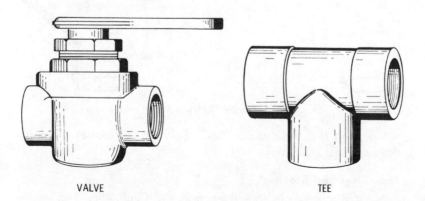

VALVE   TEE

Fig. 3. Plastic threaded fittings.

90° ELBOW

ADAPTOR

Fig. 4. Plastic epoxy fittings.

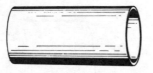
PIPE

Y

Fig. 5. *Thermo-seal* fittings.

Fig. 6. *Polyvinyl Chloride* fittings.

pylene, and Fig. 6 illustrates PVC (Polyvinyl Chloride) industrial drainage pipe and fittings.

Handling and Storing

Normal precautions should be used when unloading and storing plastic pipe. Deep scratches and gouges on the pipe surface can lead to reduced pressure-carrying capacity. Standard pipe wrenches can deform or scar threaded plastic pipe when being fabricated. Strap wrenches are recommended. Pipe being placed in a pipe vise or chuck should be wrapped at the jaw location with emery cloth or soft metal.

Store pipe in a clean area with adequate ventilation. Do not mix plastic fittings and flanges with metal-pipe components—store separately. Avoid burrs and sharp edges on metal racks. Store pipe on racks that afford continuous support to prevent sagging or draping of long lengths. Do not store or install plastic pipe near steam lines or other heat sources that could overheat or damage the pipe.

Cutting

Plastic pipe can be cut easily with a power or hand hacksaw, circular, or band saw. For best results, use fine-tooth blades with relatively little set. Carbide-tipped blades are preferable when quantities of pipe are to be cut. Pipe and tube cutters are not recommended as they might cause excessive heat and pressure that could result in cracked or irregular ends. To secure good square-end cuts, a miter box, hold-down, or jig is recommended. Remove all burrs with a fine-tooth file, deburring tool, or sharp knife. Before installation, remove all chips, burrs, filings, etc., from the inside of the pipe.

Bending

Bending leaves residual stresses in plastic pipe. The use of bends is not recommended, particularly when the line is to operate at or near maximum rated temperatures and pressures. Factory-made fittings and straight lengths of pipe give better performance.

When field bending is required for special purposes, or to provide for expansion and contraction, the following practices are recommended:

1. Seal both ends of the pipe length with a plumber's test plug and introduce sufficient air pressure to maintain ovality of the pipe during bending. The same purpose can be achieved by filling the pipe with pre-heated sand.

2. Heat the pipe uniformly by immersing in hot oil or water, or by rotating in front of a hot-air gun. Do not use an open flame.

3. When the pipe becomes soft and pliable, place in a wooden forming jig, and bend it as quickly as possible to prevent weakening or deforming. Minimum radius to which a bend should be made is 5 to 6 pipe diameters, but the initial forming bend should be slightly greater to allow for springback.

4. Keep bend in forming jig until the pipe cools and becomes rigid and then cool it quickly by immersion in water. Do not remove sand or relieve air pressure until after final cooling.

Thermoset plastics, such as glass-reinforced epoxy, cannot be field bent by heating.

Solvent Welding

A good method for joining rigid thermoplastics, such as PVC and PVDC, is by solvent welding. This method provides stronger and tighter joints than threading. Engineers have suggested the following useful pointers:

1. Use the proper solvent cement—PVC cement with PVC pipe and PVDC cement with PVDC pipe.

2. When solvent welding lighter PVC pipe, apply lightweight PVC cement to the pipe O.D. only, and not to the pipe and fitting as is done when solvent welding heavier pipe.

3. Leave a fillet bead between pipe and fitting when solvent welding PVC and PVDC piping.

4. Use a natural (hog) bristle brush for applying solvent cement. Nylon and other synthetic materials are attacked by solvents in the cement.

5. Use a 1/2" wide brush for pipe 1/2" through 1"; a 1" brush for 1-1/4" through 2" pipe, and a 2" brush for pipe 3" and larger.

6. An ordinary oil can is an excellent container for acetone-type cleaner. Excessive evaporation is prevented and the solvent is always handy.

7. Do not allow water to come into contact with solvent cement. Wrap a cloth or handkerchief around the forehead in hot weather to keep perspiration from dripping into the cement. When not using, keep the cement covered.

8. Allow solvent cement to cure 5 to 15 minutes before handling, and wait 24 hours before introducing full line pressure into a solvent-cemented piping system.

9. At the end of the day, place the brush in cleaner and cover the cement tightly. When re-using a brush, shake excess MEK cleaner out before dipping into the cement.

Threaded Joints

Temporary lines usually are installed with threaded connections. Threading reduces the effective wall thicknesses of the pipe and results in lower pressure ratings. Threaded connections should be used *only* with fairly heavy pipe.

Use *Cabot*-type *Tite-Joint* thread tape for all threaded connections, as screwed fittings tend to bind after long periods of service. Wrap tape around the male threads, overlapping about 1/4", until the entire length is covered. *Teflon*-type base thread lubricant can also be used. It is inert and retains its lubricating qualities indefinitely. Squeeze a small amount on the pipe male thread, spread with a brush, and screw the fitting onto pipe.

Fillet Welding

Fillet welding is the generally accepted practice of repairing leaks in thermoplastic piping systems. Plumbers and pipefitters learn fillet welding rapidly, as general procedures are similar to those used for welding and brazing metals. However, the following general practices are recommended by engineers and technicians.

1. Welding surfaces must be clean from dirt, oil, moisture, and loose particles of plastic material. When welding solvent-welded joints, allow the cement to cure six hours before

145

welding. Remove all excess cement residue with a knife, emery cloth, or wire brush before welding. Do not weld a joint while it is leaking, as the moisture will prevent a good bond.

2. Maintain uniform heat and pressure on rod while welding. Too much heat will char, melt, or distort the material; too much pressure on the rod tends to stretch the weld bead which may result in cracks and checks in the weld after it cools.

3. Do not splice welds by overlapping side by side. When terminating a weld, lap the bead on top of itself (not alongside) for a distance of 3/8" to 1/2".

Fig. 7. Fillet welding theromoplastic piping.

4. A single-drip leak usually can be repaired with a single bead weld; more serious leaks require full fillet welds, usually three beads and up to five beads in large-diameter pipe. When making multiple-layer welds, allow sufficient time for each pass to cool before proceeding with final welds.

5. When welding PVC or PVDC, hold the rod at an angle of 90° to the work; when welding polyethylene, polypropylene, and penton, hold the rod about 75° away from the gun, as indicated in Fig. 7.

Table 4 shows a fillet welding chart including the recommended welding temperatures.

Table 4. Fillet Thermoplastic Pipe Welding Chart

	PVC Type I	PVC Type II	PVDC	PP	PE	PENTON
Welding Temperature	500°F to 550°F	475°F to 525°F	500°F to 550°F	550°F to 600°F	500°F to 550°F	600°F to 650°F
Welding Gas	Air	Air	Air	Inert	Inert	Air
Odor Under Flame	HCL	HCL	HCL	Wax	Wax	Sweet Chlorine
Position of Rod	90°	90°	90°	75°	75°	75°
Remarks			Low weld strengths	May splash; reduce airflow		May splash; reduce airflow

Underground Installation

Depth of the ditch is not necessarily critical, except in freezing areas where it is recommended that pipe be laid well below the frost line. If the soil at the trench is unyielding (clay, as an illustration), over-excavate the trench about four inches and place a cushion of rock-free soil or coarse sand to bring the trench to final grade. When ground water is encountered, the bottom must be stabilized by over-excavating about 12 inches and filling to the grade with gravel having a maximum particle size of 1/2 inch. Keep the trench free of ground water during laying and joining, and until it is back-filled sufficiently to prevent flotation of the pipe.

Final trimming and grading must be accomplished by hand. Make sure the trench bottom is smooth and regular to avoid local bending. Do not block the pipe to grade. The first 8 to 12 inches of back-fill material must be free of rocks and other cutting or sharp objects. Fine sand, clay, silt, and frozen soil lumps are not recommended for backfilling. Assemble plastic pipe in sections above ground and then lower into the trench. It is recommended that several lengths of pipe be placed in the trench bottom so that the pipe will not be cocked or canted while a joint is being made. When solvent-welded joints are used, it is recommended that backfilling be delayed about five minutes after completion of the joint to allow the cement to take initial set. Pressure testing is often completed prior to backfilling.

During backfilling, it is recommended that the pipe be at operating temperature and pressure if possible. This practice prevents pipe deformation due to expansion. Compensation for thermal expansion in buried plastic pipe can be achieved by snaking the line from side to side in the trench. One cycle for each 40 feet or less is satisfactory in most cases.

Expansion in Plastic Pipe

When total temperature change is less than 30°F, special provisions for accommodating thermal expansion are not generally required, particularly when the line includes several directional changes which provide some inherent flexibility. Exercise caution with threaded connections, however, as they are more vulnerable to failure by bending stresses than are solvent-welded joints. When expansion cannot be assumed by regular dimensional changes, several methods to compensate for expansion are available. One is to fabricate an offset or expansion loop using elbows and straight pipe joined by solvent welding.

Another is the use of an expansion joint. The latter is particularly recommended for large-diameter pipe and where space for offset lines is limited. An expansion joint is basically two tubes, one telescoping inside the other. The outer tube is to be firmly anchored and the inner tube allowed to move with a piston-like action as the attached pipe expands or contracts. In long runs (15 feet or more) it is recommended the pipe line be anchored at each change of direction so the expansion movement in the pipe can be directed squarely into the expansion joint.

Alignment of expansion joints is important, as binding may result if the pipe is canted or cocked and does not move in the same plane as the joint. It is recommended that guide loops be installed approximately one foot from each end of each expansion joint. If there is any doubt about expansion joints for plastic pipe, contact a representative of the piping company or the manufacturing company for information.

Supporting Plastic Pipe

Most companies recommend that thermoplastic piping be supported at intervals roughly 1/2 to 1/4 of that normally required for steel pipe. Supports and hangers can be clamp, saddle, angle, spring, or other standard types. Broad and smooth bearing surfaces are better than narrow or sharp contacts, as they minimize danger of stress concentration and physical damage. Continuous support in channel iron often is provided for lines operating at high temperatures or handling hazardous liquids at high temperatures. Angle irons suspended with clevis hangers have also been used successfully. Avoid clamping the pipe so as to prevent endwise movement needed to take care of thermal expansion. Rigid clamping is advisable at valves and fittings located near sharp changes in direction when the line is subjected to wide temperature changes.

Do not lay plastic pipe on steam lines or other high-temperature surfaces. With the exception of couplings, support all plastic fittings individually, and brace valves against operating torque. Generally, vertical runs are supported by spring hangers and guided with rings or long U-bolts which restrict movement of the rise to one plane. It is sometimes helpful to support a long riser with a saddle at the bottom. General residential plastic piping is available for complete piping sytems. A plastic drain-waste-vent pipe and fittings system offers many advantages. It is corrosion proof, can't rust, corrode, or rot. Ordinary household chemicals and effluents do not affect it. A smooth interior has a tendency to eliminate buildup of deposits. Plastic pipe is also available for installation with septic systems, although requirements of local plumbing codes must be investigated prior to purchase and installation.

SUMMARY

The quantity of water that will be discharged through a pipe depends primarily on the head and also upon the diameter of the pipe, the character of the interior surface, and the number and shape of the bends. The head may be either the actual distance between the levels of the surface of water in a reservoir and the point of discharge, or it may be caused by mechanically applied pressure, as by pumping, in which case the head is calculated as the vertical distance corresponding to the pressure.

The term "wrought-iron pipe" is often used indiscriminately to designate all butt- or lap-welded pipe whether made from wrought iron or steel. A large percentage of the "wrought pipe" now used is made of steel. Formerly, wrought iron was preferred for the best classes of work, but records of installation and tests show that steel pipe is equal to wrought-iron pipe for general work.

The use of plastic pipe has increased tremendously in recent years. Originally, plastic pipe was used for farm water systems and lawn sprinkling systems, but now it is used for gas distribution, waste disposals, and for industrial and residential plumbing applications.

REVIEW QUESTIONS

1. What are the three grades of thickness in wrought-iron pipe?

2. How is plastic pipe joined?

3. What is the lightest plastic-pipe material?

4. What type of thermoplastic material is used for corrosive fluids?

5. How should plastic piping be stored?

CHAPTER 6

Tools

On ordinary jobs only a few tools are required by the plumber, but for all the operations performed in plumbing work, a considerable number are required. In this chapter only the ordinary or commonly used tools are considered. Additional and special tools are covered in the chapters pertaining to the work for which they are designed.

With respect to use, plumbers' tools may be classified as:

1. Guiding and testing tools.
   a. Straightedge.
   b. Square.
   c. Level.
   d. Plumb bob.

2. Marking tools.
   a. Chalk line.
   b. Pencil.
   c. Scratch awl.
   d. Scriber.
   e. Compasses and dividers.

3. Measuring tools.
   a. Rule.
   b. Tape.

4. Holding tools.
   a. Pliers.

    b. Clamps.

    c. Vises.

    d. Wrenches.

5. Toothed cutting tools.
   a. Saws.
   b. Files.
   c. Rasps.

6. Scraping and grinding tools.
   a. Scrapers.
   b. Sand paper.
   c. Automatic grinders.

7. Sharp-edge cutting tools.
   a. Chisels.
   b. Cold chisels.
   c. Knife.
   d. Wire cutters.
   e. Shears.
   f. Hatchet.

8. Boring tools.
   a. Bits.
   b. Drills.
   c. Countersinks.
   d. Reamers.
   e. Tap borer.

9. Threading tools.
   a. Dies.
   b. Taps.
   c. Stocks.
   d. Pipe vise.
   e. Pipe cutters.

10. Fastening tools.
   a. Hammers.
   b. Screw drivers.
   c. Wrenches.

11. Bending tools.
    a. Hickey.
    b. Bending pins.
    c. Dummy.
    d. Sand plugs.
    e. Bobbins.

12. Soldering and jointing tools.
    a. Bits.
    b. Solder pot.
    c. Ladle.
    d. Tank iron.
    e. Soldering irons.

13. Heating tools.
    a. Fire pots.
    b. Torches.

14. Cleaning tools.
    a. Force cups.
    b. Hand augers.
    c. Automatic snakes, etc.

From the list, it will be seen that the work of the plumber, at times, overlaps that of the carpenter. The roughing out work for the reception of the piping and fixtures, though usually done by a carpenter, is sometimes done by the plumber, especially in remote sections.

STRAIGHTEDGES

This tool is used to guide the pencil or scriber in marking a straight line, and in testing a faced surface, such as the edge of a board, to determine if it is straight. Anything having an edge known to be straight, such as the edge of a steel square, may be used; however, a regular straightedge is preferable. It may be made either of wood or steel and be from a few inches to several feet in length. For ordinary work, a plumber can make a line sufficiently accurate from a strip of good straight-grained wood, but for accurate work, a steel straightedge should be used. Wood is objectionable in work of precision because of its tendency to warp or spring out of shape.

SQUARES

This tool is a 90° or right-angle standard and is used for marking or testing work. There are several types of squares, as:

1. Try (or trying) square.
2. Combined try and miter square.
3. Combination square.

Try Squares

In England, this is called the *trying square,* but here simply *try square.* It is called try square because of its frequent use as a

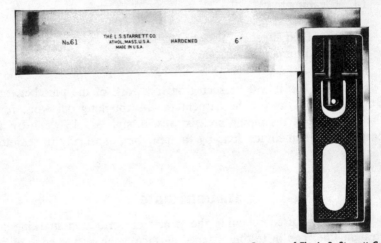

Courtesy of The L. S. Starrett Co.

Fig. 1. A typical try square.

testing tool when squaring up mill-planed stock. The ordinary try square used by carpenters consist of a steel *blade* set at right angles to the inside face of the *stock* in which it is held. A typical square is shown in Fig. 1.

154

Miter and Combined Try Squares

The term *miter,* strictly speaking, signifies any angle except a right angle, but as applied to squares it usually means an angle of 45°. In the miter square, the blade, as in the try square, is

Courtesy of The L. S. Starrett Co.

Fig. 2. A typical combination square.

permanently set, but at an angle of 45° with the stock. A try square may be made into a combined try and miter square, as shown in Fig. 2, when the end of the stock to which the blade is fastened is faced off at 45°.

LEVELS

This tool is used for both guiding and testing; to guide in bringing the work to a horizontal or vertical position, and to test the accuracy and levelness of the completed construction and piping. Levels are made in a variety of types and shapes, but all are used for the same purpose. Some of the types and uses are indicated in Fig. 3.

Engineers' and Plumbers' Levels

This level is designed for engineers, plumbers, and other skilled workmen. It combines three uses in one—a fixed level, a plumb, and an adjustable incline level. The incline level tube has a hinged

155

Courtesy The L. S. Starrett Co.

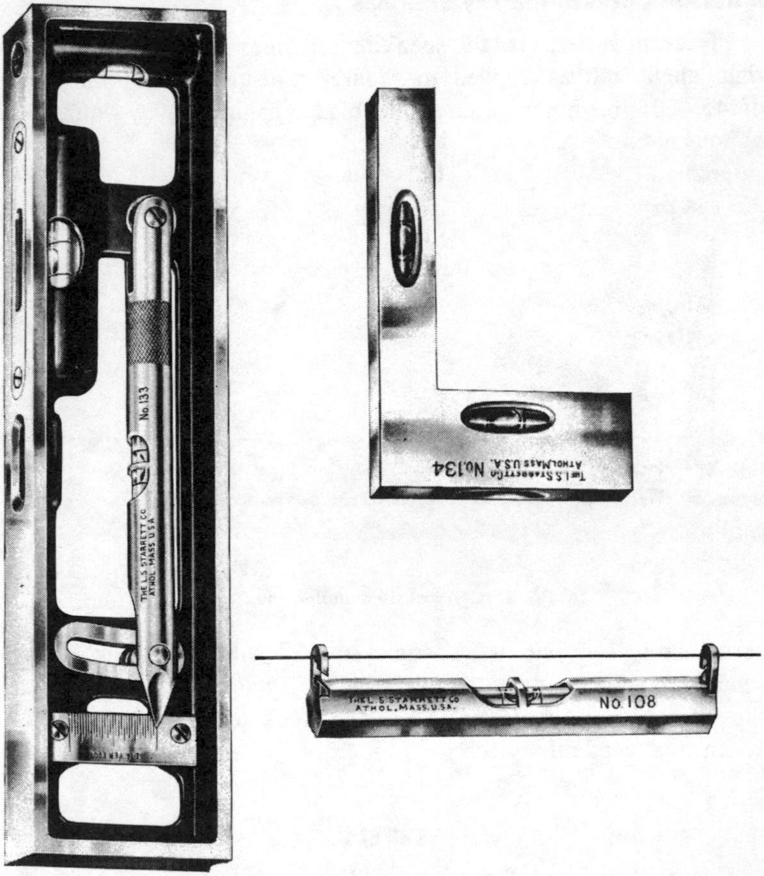

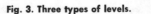

Fig. 3. Three types of levels.

mounting inside the level frame. After placing the level on any inclined surface it is adjusted to the *level* position. The degree of incline is then indicated by the pointer at the end of the level tube and read off a plate graduated in 1/16-inch per foot and reading up to 2 inches per foot incline. They are obtainable in sizes 10 to 15 inches in length.

Cross and Test Levels

The cross and test level and plumb is a $2'' \times 3''$ level particularly valuable for plumbing, approximate squaring, and leveling work. The level has two vials at right angles for cross-test leveling without moving the tool, and a plumb level at the top for checking squareness. It weighs three ounces and is of bright nickel finish.

Line Levels

The line levels, generally made of aluminum, are used in laying foundations, tile and steel pipe, cement and brick walls, determining grades, and working ditches. It can also be used as a surface level. The lightness of this level tends to eliminate sag in the line. It is made from 3/8 inch hexagonal stock, 3 inches long, and weighing about 1/2 ounce. It may be conveniently carried in the pocket. A luminous level glass with a yellowish fluid, which is preferable in line levels, is furnished with this type level. The level glass has two graduated lines to check true level and a metal guard to prevent breakage.

PLUMB BOBS

The word *plumb* means *perpendicular to the plane of the horizon,* and since the plane of the horizon is perpendicular to the direction of gravity at any given point, the force due to gravity is utilized to obtain a vertical line in the device known as a plumb bob, shown in Fig. 4. The plumb bob is made from solid steel, bored and filled with mercury to provide a low center of gravity and great weight in proportion to its short length and small diameter. A no-roll hex head prevents rolling when the plumb bob is set down. Since the point is removable, it can be easily replaced if broken or worn. An outstanding feature which results in the bob hanging perfectly true is the device for fastening the string without a knot to tie or untie, by simply drawing it into the specially shaped slotted neck at the top.

CHALK LINES

The special use of this device is to mark a long straight line between two points that are too far apart to permit the use of a

Fig. 4. A typical plumb bob.

Courtesy The L. S. Starrett Co.

square or straight edge. The line consists of a string cord strong enough to withstand heavy usage. It is rubbed with chalk and then stretched between the two points. When the string is taut it is pulled up and let spring back, thus marking a chalked line on the surface of the work. Note the right and wrong way to use a chalk line, as shown in Fig. 5.

MARKING OR SCRATCH AWLS

This consists of a short piece of round steel, pointed at one end, and the other end fixed in a convenient handle. A scratch awl is an inexpensive *form of scriber* and is used in laying out fine work where a lead pencil mark would be too coarse for the required degree of precision. The scratch awl is shown in Fig. 6.

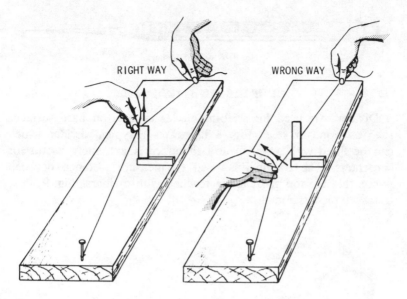

Fig. 5. Right and wrong way to use the chalk line.

Fig. 6. A typical scratch awl.

Scribers

This is a tool of extreme precision which, while intended espe-cially for machinists, should be in the tool kit of all mechanics. A scriber is a hardened steel tool with a sharp point designed to mark very fine lines. The most convenient form of scriber is the pocket or telescoping type shown in Fig. 7, the construction ren-dering it safe to carry in the pocket.

159

Fig. 7. A typical scriber.

DIVIDERS AND TRAMMELS

Dividers are used for scribing circles or arcs on hard surfaces such as wood or steel. Fig. 8 illustrates a typical divider which can be fitted with a pencil and therefore is extremely useful for carpenters. The trammel is used to measure distance between points that are too great to be reached with dividers. Fig. 9 illustrates a typical trammel.

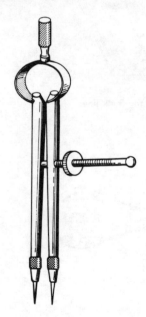

Fig. 8. Dividers used to scribe circles.

PUNCHES

Punches are essential in plumbing and pipe fitting work. Center punches are used to pin-point drilling centers, and drive pin punches are used for making holes where drilling is not necessary. The punches illustrated in Fig. 10 have knurled finger grips with points ground at the proper angle to give maximum service. Tops are especially tempered to prevent the head from fracturing.

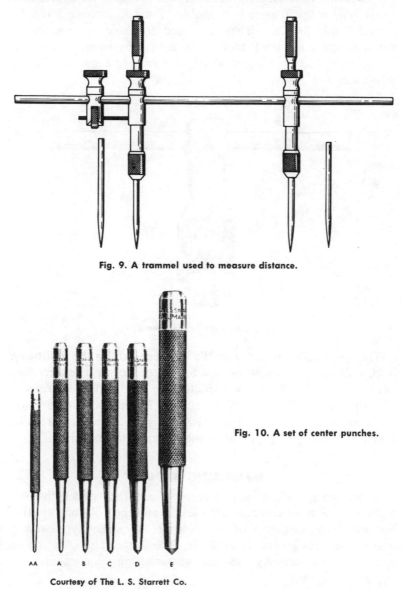

Fig. 9. A trammel used to measure distance.

Fig. 10. A set of center punches.

AA   A   B   C   D   E

Courtesy of The L. S. Starrett Co.

161

T-HANDLE TAP WRENCHES

Occasionally, it may be necessary to work in close quarters where only a small space is available. T-handle wrenches can be used for this purpose. They are used for holding taps, drills, reamers, and other small tools to be turned by hand. The length of the body, and the tap and shank size vary in capacity. Fig. 11 shows a tool of this type.

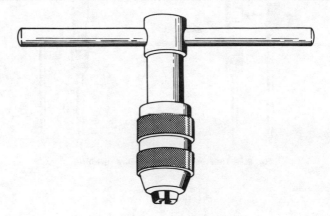

Fig. 11. A T-handle tap wrench.

The construction is such that the jaws conform to the tool being held, making it rigid and less apt to become loose. The wrenches have a sliding handle which is frictionally held. This feature permits the handle to be positioned so that leverage can be applied when working in close quarters. Ratchet-type T-handles are also available, making this type of wrench even more useful.

MEASURING TAPES

Measuring tapes can be purchased in a variety of lengths and types, but the most common are the 50- and the 100-foot lengths. For measuring distances of 6 to 10 feet, a pocket type with a pushbutton spring wind is available. The longer tapes, as shown in Fig. 12, are normally used for measuring pipe for installations requiring long runs.

162

Fig. 12. A 50-foot steel
measuring tape.

Courtesy of The L. S. Starrett Co.

VISES

The essential features of a vise are rigidity, weight, strength, accurate fit, and smoothly working parts. Rigidity and weight are required to make effective the effort expended on the work held in the vise. The *anvil quality,* or inertia sufficient to effectively hold a piece of work solidly against a blow, is a most important quali-

Courtesy of The L. S. Starrett Co.
Fig. 13. A typical bench vise.

163

fication in a vise, and a suitable mass of iron is just as necessary to supply this inertia as to supply strength against rupture. It is, of course, essential that a vise be strong enough to withstand any strain that may be legitimately put upon it. The common bench vise is illustrated in Fig. 13 and a standard drill-press vise in Fig. 14.

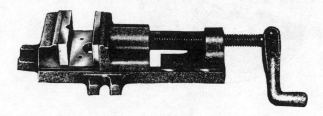

Fig. 14. A standard drill-press vise.

There is probably no tool in a shop subjected to more abuse than a vise. A frequent cause of vise breakage is the clamping near one end of a long piece of work which may thus have considerable overhang. Many times the operator, instead of hunting up a stick or other support to keep the free end from dropping, will attempt to hold it by excessive pressure between the vise jaws. If the operation involves any considerable hammering, the service exacted of that vise is most severe. One cause of minor breakage is the clamping of a hard piece of metal so that the pressure is concentrated upon a small area near the margins or corners of the hardened jaw face. If the jaw is hardened enough to resist battering or indentation, a piece is almost sure to be broken out, leaving an unsightly notch.

A very common fault of vise users is their failure to keep the screw lubricated. The thread on many vise nuts has practically disappeared from this cause. The front jaw should be occasionally detached from the vise, turned over, and the screw lubricated its entire working length. When this is done at reasonable intervals, the screw and nut will wear indefinitely. The use of vises having smooth faces for their gripping jaws is not nearly as extensive as it would be with a better comprehension of their capabilities.

FILES AND RASPS

By definition, a *file* is a steel instrument having its surface covered with a sharp-edged furrows or teeth, and used for abrading or smoothing other substances such as metal and wood. A *rasp* is a very coarse file and differs from the ordinary file in that its teeth consist of projecting points instead of V-shaped projections extending across the face of the file.

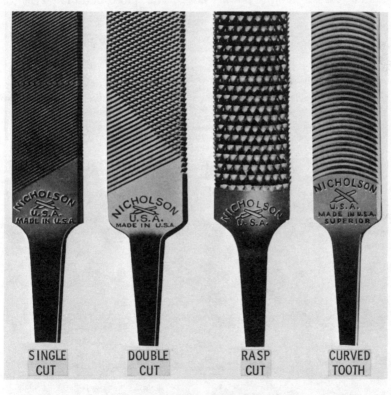

SINGLE CUT   DOUBLE CUT   RASP CUT   CURVED TOOTH

Fig. 15. Various types of files and rasps.

Files are used for many purposes by wood workers. Fig. 15 shows a variety of files. The teeth of the mill file leave a smooth surface. They are particularly adapted to filing and sharpening mill saws, and mowing and reaping machine cutters. Rasps are generally used for cutting away or smoothing wood, or for finishing off the rough edge left in a circular hole cut with the keyhole saw. The ordinary wood rasp is rougher or coarser than that used by cabinetmakers.

SAWS

There are many types of saws that can be obtained for a particular use, including power saws. The most common type of

Fig. 16. A typical handsaw.

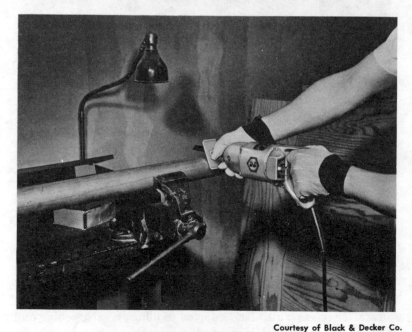

Fig. 17. A portable power hacksaw.

Courtesy of Black & Decker Co.
Fig. 18. A portable power drill using a high-speed hole saw.

handsaw is shown in Fig. 16. Portable power reciprocating saws are used for many purposes, both with hacksaw-type blades and with high-speed hole saws, as shown in Figs. 17 and 18. The hole saws are used with drill presses for shop use and with portable drills on job sites. Type of blade selection, particularly for hacksaws, are governed by the type of material being cut.

SCRAPERS

There are two kinds of scrapers—those intended for wood, and those for metal. The particular kind of scraper most commonly used by plumbers is known as the *shave hook,* as shown in Fig. 19. They are made in various shapes, the one shown being for general use in brightening metal surfaces preliminary to soldering or wiping joints. Fig. 20 shows the method of using this tool.

167

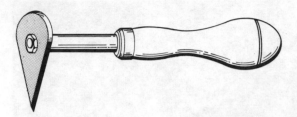

Fig. 19. A shave hook used for brightening metals.

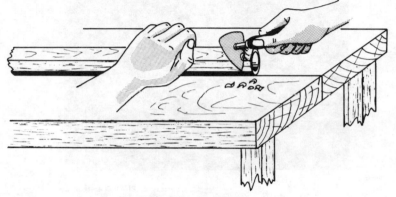

Fig. 20. Method of using the shave hook.

CHISELS

In carpentry, the chisel is an indispensable tool. The plumber frequently must use the chisel in cutting away wood members to make room for pipes. A chisel should be absolutely flat on the back (the side not beveled). An inferior chisel is ground off on the back near the cutting edge, with the result that it tends to follow the grain of the wood, splitting it off unevenly, because the user cannot properly control the chisel. The flat back allows the chisel to take off the very finest shaving, and where a thick cut is desired, it will not strike too deep. This is a point to be found in good chisels.

Chisels are made of selected steel with the blade almost imperceptibly widening toward the cutting edge. The blades are oil tempered and carefully tested. The ferrule and blade of the socket

168

chisel are so carefully welded together that they form a single piece. Handles are generally of very durable plastic materials, although some chisels have highly-finished hickory handles.

In honing a chisel, use a good grade oil stone. Pour a few drops of machine oil on the stone, or if no machine oil is available, use lard oil or sperm oil. The best results are obtained by using a carborundum stone. The carborundum cuts faster than most other abrasives. Hold the chisel in the right hand and grasp the edges of the stone with the fingers of the left hand to keep it from slipping; place the stone on a bench and block it so it cannot move. Both hands will thus be free to use in honing. In this case, grasp the chisel in the right hand where the shoulder joins the socket; place the middle and forefinger on the blade near the cutting edge; rub the chisel on the stone away from you, being careful to keep the original bevel.

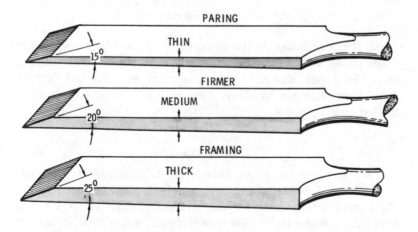

Fig. 21. Illustrating the bevel angle for different type chisels.

Never sharpen the chisel on the back or flat side; this should be kept perfectly flat. For paring, the taper should be long and thin, about 15°. The longer the bevel on the cutting edge, the easier the chisel will work, and the easier it is to hone it. In sharpening a firmer chisel, it should be ground at an angle of not less than 20° to 25° (see Fig. 21). In honing a chisel, the taper should

169

be carefully maintained, and unless the back is kept flat, it will be impossible to work to a line. Bevel-edge chisels are more easily sharpened than the plain edge, as there is not so much steel to be removed. In case the chisel is badly "nicked," it will have to be ground on a grindstone before honing. Never use a file. Be sure

Courtesy of Millers Falls Co.
Fig. 22. A typical chisel sharpener.

to use plenty of water on the stone so as not to injure the temper of the chisel, and be particular to keep the original taper of the bevel. After grinding, hone on an oilstone as instructed. Where chisel sharpeners are available (see Fig. 22) these are used in the sharpening process.

AUGERS

These are used for boring holes from 1/2 inch up to 2 inches. The sizes are listed in 16ths; thus, a 2-inch auger is listed as 32. When made with a shank for use in a brace, this style of auger is commonly called a bit. To sharpen the spur, hold the bit in the left hand with the twist resting on the edge of the bench. Turn the bit around until the spur to be sharpened comes uppermost. File the side of the spur next to the screw, carefully keeping the original bevel. File lightly until a fine burr shows on the outside, which is carefully removed by a slight brush with a file. This will result in a fine cutting edge.

To sharpen the cutter, hold the bit firmly in the left hand with the worn point down on the edge of the bench. Be careful to preserve the original bevel and take off the burr or rough edge. Never sharpen the outside of the spur. It is rarely necessary or advisable to sharpen the worm. However, it may often be improved if battered, by using a three-cornered file, carefully manipulated, using one of a size that fits the thread. A half-round file is best for the lip and, with careful handling, may be used for the spur.

TWIST DRILLS

These are for drilling small holes where the ordinary auger might split the wood. They come either with square or round shanks, and in sizes from 1/16" to 5/8", or more. A drill differs from an auger due to the absence of a screw and a less acute cutting angle of the lip; hence, there is no tendency to split the wood. The tool does not pull itself in by a taper screw but enters by external pressure. For many operations, especially where the smaller drills are used, as in drilling nail holes through boat ribs and planking, hand drills are preferable.

POWER TOOLS

In order to increase production and efficiency, power tools are used both in the shop and at job sites. When at locations where no electrical source is available, power is supplied by batteries or generators. Fig. 23 illustrates a typical battery-operated 1/4-inch general-purpose drill. Attachments are available for power drills which convert them into buffers, jig saws, orbital sanders, right-angle drills, drill presses, bench sanders, bench grinders, and circular saws. Electric drills vary in type and size from the very small 1/4-inch to the heavy-duty 1-inch chuck type.

Portable Grinders

Portable grinders are used for smoothing welds, grinding off rivets, and many other purposes both on the job and in the shop. They are particularly useful in demolition work where it is necessary to remove old fixtures or boilers. Heavily rusted bolts or tight fittings can be ground loose and heavy straps cut.

171

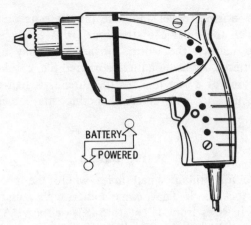

Fig. 23. Illustrating a portable power drill that can be
operated on electricity or battery.

Power Hacksaw

Power hacksaws (Fig. 24) are used for cutting metal stock of
all types in shop work. Flat and rolled stock, angle iron, pipe and
fittings, and angle cuts can all be made with jigs on the power
hacksaw. Special cutting saws are required for some materials, as
shown in Table 1.

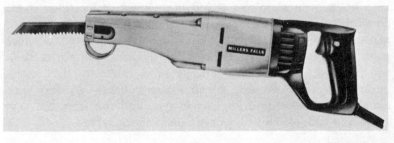

Courtesy of Millers Falls Co.
Fig. 24. An electric portable power saw.

POWER RODDING EQUIPMENT

Kitchen sinks, toilets, and other fixture drain lines may become
clogged as a result of an accumulation of scale, rust, grease, silt,

Table 1.   Power Hacksaw Cutting Chart

Material	Teeth per Inch	Strokes per Minute	Weight or Pressure, Lbs.
Aluminum Alloy	4-6	150	60
Aluminum, Pure	4-6	150	60
Brass Castings, Soft	6-10	150	60
Brass Castings, Hard	6-10	135	60
Bronze Castings	6-10	135	125
Cast Iron	6-10	135	125
Copper, Drawn	6-10	135	125
*Carbon Tool Steel	6-10	90	125
*Cold Rolled Steel	4-6	135	150
*Drill Rod	10	90	125
*High Speed Steel	6-10	90	125
*Machinery Steel	4-6	135	150
Manganese Bronze	6-10	90	60
*Malleable Iron	6-10	90	125
*Nickel Silver	6-10	60	150
*Nickel Steel	6-10	90	150
Pipe, Iron	10-14	135	125
Slate	6-10	90	125
*Structural Steel	6-10	135	125
Tubing, Brass	14	135	60
*Tubing, Steel	14	135	60

*Use cutting compound or coolant.

etc. For kitchen sinks and toilets, a *snake* rodding line is used for cleaning. An electric lightweight power rodder (Fig. 25) is used to clean the lines. The motor of the device rotates the cable for cutting. An open hook-on cable is used for lavatories, bath traps, and toilets, and it is generally not necessary to disconnect fixture parts and lines for cleaning. Interchangeable blade-end cable is supplied with the machine for cleaning sink and grease lines up to 2 inches in diameter and 35 feet in length. If the cable is removed, the *electric snake* can be used at slow speed as a drill for tile and wall board and for buffing or sanding.

Although many sanitary sewer lines are cleaned and rodded with hand-operated steel tapes and rods, most work is accomplished with automated cable-type power rodders. These portable one-man operated units (Fig. 26) clean sewers and pipe up to 200 feet long with a powerful motor-driven cable. The unit cuts stubborn tree roots that block sewers, and restores normal flow in lines from 3″ to 10″ in diameter where stoppages have occured from

Courtesy of O'Brien Mfg. Corp.
Fig. 25. Illustrating an electric sewer-snake rodding line.

sand, dirt, grease, rust, or scale. The unit is supplied with heavy 3/4″ flexible steel cable that is power rotated for cutting.

PIPE-THREADING DIES

The greatest difficulty experienced in threading pipe is due to the use of dies which are inadequate to properly perform the work expected of them. In order to obtain good results in threading any metal, the die must be made to *cut*—not *push*. A die which pushes the metal off, instead of cutting it freely, causes the threads to break out of the die. Typical dies are illustrated in Fig. 27. To get good results at one cut, experience shows that a die should have a suitable number of chasers, the approximate number being determined by the size of the die.

174

Courtesy of O'Brien Mfg. Corp.

Fig. 26. Heavy-duty electrical sewer-snake rodding line.

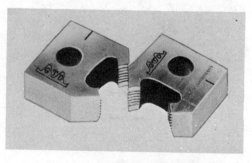

Courtesy of Greenfield Tap & Die Co.

Fig. 27. Two-piece adjustable pipe die.

PIPE STOCK

The pipe dies just described are placed in a frame work called a stock (Fig. 28) which is provided with two hand bars for turning. The stock has various size collars designed to fit the different sized pipes.

175

Fig. 28. Illustrating a typical die
stock.

Courtesy of Ridge Tool Co.

PIPE VISE

By definition, a pipe vise is a gripping appliance for holding
pipes while being threaded or cut, having two V-shaped serrated
jaws sliding within one another. The grip is applied or released

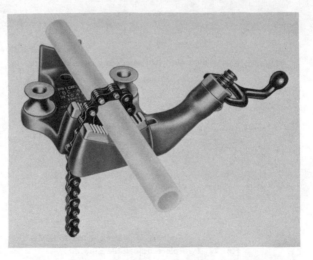

Courtesy of Ridge Tool Co.
Fig. 29. Pipe vise.

by means of a screw and toggle, as shown in Fig. 29. There are
other types of pipe vises which are particularly adapted to special
jobs and circumstances. These include chain vises, post yoke vises,
top-screw post chain vises, stand yoke vises, and stand chain vises.

176

PIPE-THREADING MACHINES

For shop work where great quantities of pipe are threaded, and especially for large work, machines are necessary. These may be either hand- or power-operated. They are constructed with a view of saving time and labor. Of course, with the hand machine, the time consumed in threading pipe depends upon the activity and experience of the man. As usually constructed, they are so arranged that when cutting off pipe, the dies are opened for the pipe to pass through (without their being removed from the machine) by a simple motion of a handwheel or lever. The gears and bearings

Fig. 30. Automatic power threading machine.

Courtesy of Ridge Tool Co.

are enclosed in an oil chamber, thus, keeping the bearings lubricated and preventing chips or dirt from getting into the working parts. Fig. 30 illustrates a power-driven automatic threading machine. It can be mounted on a bench, truck, or stand. The chuck operates forward or in reverse and has replaceable jaw inserts. It is equipped with a 1/2-hp, 115-volt, universal, reversible motor. The capacity for pipe is 1/8" through 2", and 1/4" through 2" for bolts and rod. A stand is obtainable for this machine which makes it portable. The base has folding legs and a tray.

PIPE TAP

By definition, a pipe tap is a conical screw made of hardened steel, and grooved longitudinally, for cutting threads in nuts. Various examples of pipe taps are shown in Fig. 31.

177

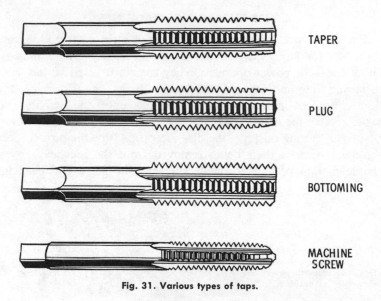

Fig. 31. Various types of taps.

PIPE CUTTERS

A pipe cutter is an instrument for cutting pipes, as shown in Fig. 32. The cutter consists of a bent lever, partially encircling the pipe, on which one or more cutting discs are mounted, the

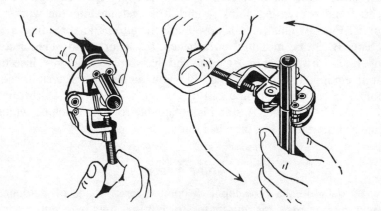

Fig. 32. Typical tube or pipe cutter and method of using the tool.

pressure and feed of the cutting discs being regulated by a screw as the lever is rotated around the pipe.

PIPE REAMERS

Several types of tapered reamers are available for use both in hand-reaming and in machine-reaming operations. Burring reamers are designed for removing the internal burrs caused by cutting pipe (Fig. 33). The straight-shank burring reamer may be used in an

Fig. 33. Burring reamer for removing burrs caused by cutting pipe.

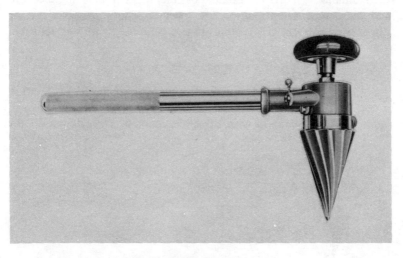

Fig. 34. Ratchet burring reamer.

179

electric drill. Burring reamers are also used for countersinking and for enlarging holes in sheet metal. A ratchet burring reamer, shown in Fig. 34, may also be used for enlarging holes in sheet metal, countersinking, etc.

PIPE-BENDING TOOLS

There are a variety of devices for bending pipe, both power- and hand-operated. One of the most common pipe benders is illustrated in Fig. 35. This lever-type bender is versatile, accurate, and easy-to-use. Correctly measured, bends will be accurate to blueprint

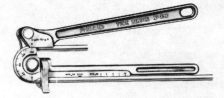

Fig. 35. A lever-type tube bender.

dimensions within plus-minus 1/32″. A scale on the link eliminates extra measuring and assures fast tube positioning for accurate finished dimensions. To eliminate possible hand injury, handles are held wide apart when making 180° bends. There are six sizes for soft or hard copper, brass, aluminum, steel, and stainless-steel tube.

TUBE CUTTERS AND REAMERS

Both the plumber and pipe fitter are involved in the installation of copper, brass, aluminum, and plastic tubing, as well as thin-wall conduit. Tubing cutters with attached reamers are often used for

Fig. 36. Tubing cutter with fold-in reamer.

Courtesy of Ridge Tool Co.

180

the cutting of the tubing. This type of tool is shown in Fig. 36. They are efficient and can be easily carried to the job site. This cutter is 5" long, features a spare cutter wheel in the handle and has a fold-in reamer. The frame is lightweight, high-strength aluminum alloy. It cuts copper, brass, aluminum tubing, and thin-wall conduit. The rollers smooth the tubing, ready for soldering.

FLARING TOOLS

In order to provide flares on tubing when fittings are to be attached for water, heating, or refrigeration, a flaring tool is used. The end of the tubing is placed into the device and a flaring cone which is attached is pressured into the end of the tube producing a flare. These tools have five to seven sizes for various diameter piping depending on the pipe size and the degree of flare desired. Fig. 37 shows the tool with a hand-turn screw-type cone.

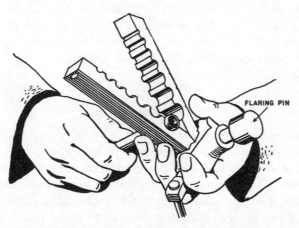

FLARING PIN

Fig. 37. Flaring tool for use with various tube diameters.

HAMMERS

The hammer is an important tool in any line of mechanical work, and there are numerous types to meet the varied conditions of use. Good hammers are made of the best steel, carefully forged, hardened, and tempered.

181

SCREWDRIVERS

These tools are designed to insert or remove screws. They have, however, been used as a substitute for many other tools. There are several classes of screwdrivers used in the average workshop, such as:

1. Plain.
2. Ratchet.
3. Offset.
4. Phillips.

The plain or standard screwdriver is very similar to a chisel and differs from the latter chiefly in the working end, which is blunt. There are very few screwdrivers with correctly shaped blade tips. The sides which enter the slot in the screw are usually tapered. This is done so that the end will fit into slots of widely varying sizes.

When using a screwdriver having a tapered blade tip, a force is set up due to the taper which tends to push the end of the tool out of the slot. Accordingly, it is better to have several sizes with properly shaped parallel sides than to depend on one size with tapered sides for all sizes of screws.

WRENCHES

There are on the market a multiplicity of wrenches of many kinds and patterns for every conceivable use. The wrench, though it may not be so considered, can be a dangerous tool when very great force is applied to start an obstinate nut. Often, under such conditions, the jaws may slip off the nut, resulting in injury to the workman by violent contact with some metal part.

There are five general classes of wrenches:

1. Plain box and open-end.
2. Adjustable.
3. Socket.
4. Hex.
5. Strap and chain.
6. Stillson (Pipe).

Open-end wrenches are of the solid nonadjustable type with openings in each end, as shown in Fig. 38. These are customarily made in "sets," with the average set containing about ten wrenches, with openings that range from 5/16-inch to 1-inch in width.

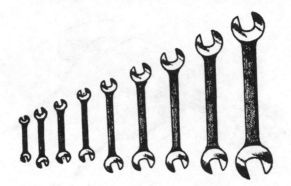

Fig. 38. A set of open-end wrenches.

Box-end wrenches are so called because they "box" or completely surround the nut or bolt head. Their usefulness is partly based on their ability to operate in close quarters. Because of their design, there is very little chance of the wrench slipping off the nut. As noted in Fig. 39, there are 12 notches arranged in a

Fig. 39. Typical box-end wrench.

circle. A wrench of this type is called a 12-point wrench and can be used to continuously loosen or tighten a nut with a handle rotation of only 15°, compared to the 60° swing needed by the open-end wrench if it is reversed after every swing.

Adjustable wrenches are shaped somewhat similarly to open-end wrenches, the difference being that one jaw is adjustable as noted in Fig. 40. A spiral worm adjustment in the handle permits

183

the width of the jaw to be varied from zero to one-half inch or more, depending on the size of the wrench.

Socket wrenches are so called because the wrench is made in two or more parts; that is, a socket which fits the bolt or nut, and

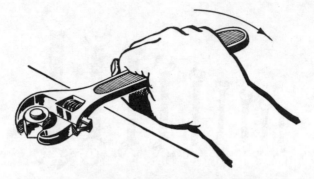

Fig. 40. Adjustable wrench and method of tightening nut.

a detachable handle or lever to fit the socket in turning. The modern socket wrench (Fig. 41) is usually equipped with a ratchet mechanism similar to that used in certain hand braces for

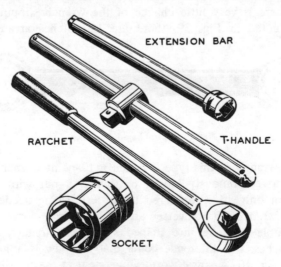

Fig. 41. Socket wrench and various handles.

boring holes in tight corners. This permits the use of the wrench in locations where the handle travel is limited, besides making it unnecessary to shift the socket on the nut or bolt for each pull on the handle.

A Stillson wrench is an adjustable pipe wrench and differs principally from other types in that it has toothed jaws which will assist in getting a firm grip on pipes and shafting. Pipe wrenches of this type will work in one direction only. To tighten a pipe joint, for example, the open end of the wrench must face in the opposite direction to that which loosens or unscrews the joint.

SOLDERING TOOLS

Soldering may be defined as the process of joining two metal parts together by a metal called solder. Solder is an alloy of lead and tin and has a lower melting point than either of its components or the metals to be joined. Solders which melt readily are termed soft solders, while those which melt at a red heat are termed hard solders. The process of soldering consist of cleaning the surfaces to be joined, and heating them to the soldering temperature by any suitable means, such as:

1. Soldering irons (plain and electric).
2. Gas flame.
3. Blowtorch.

The essentials for any soldering job are clean metal surfaces, correct flux, good quality solder, and sufficient heat.

The purpose of the soldering flux (which is generally rosin or zinc chloride) is to remove any grease or oxide present on the materials to be soldered. The solder is then melted into the joint and the joint smoothed over and finished by the use of a copper-tipped soldering iron or other heating means.

Soldering Irons

Soldering irons, such as shown in Fig. 42, are generally used for small soldering work. Made with a copper tip, these tools must be properly *tinned* or coated with solder and maintained in a clean

185

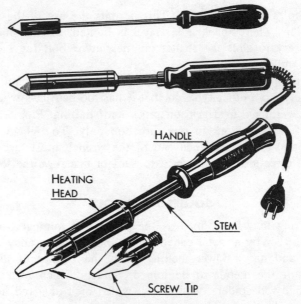

HANDLE

HEATING
HEAD

STEM

SCREW TIP

Fig. 42. Various types of soldering irons.

condition before they can be used efficiently. Tinning consists of filing the surface of the tip to a bright, smooth finish, heating it to a temperature sufficient to melt the solder, and then applying a small portion of solder and rosin to the surface of the tip. This process will form a tinned surface on all sides.

Torches and Lead-Melting Devices

For general soldering work, a gasoline torch (Fig. 43) can be used to heat soldering irons. A propane torch (Fig. 44) is often used for soldering, particularly when the work is performed on copper and brass pipe. Propane torches are easy to operate. The gas jet is turned on, a spark lighter or match is used and immediately you have a 2250° flame. There are a number of attachments, such as a blow-torch burner head, flame spreader, or soldering tip, that can be readily obtained.

Portable gasoline furnaces (Fig. 45), although generally used for melting lead, also work very well for heating soldering irons. For melting lead, a pot and ladle made of cast iron is used (Fig.

186

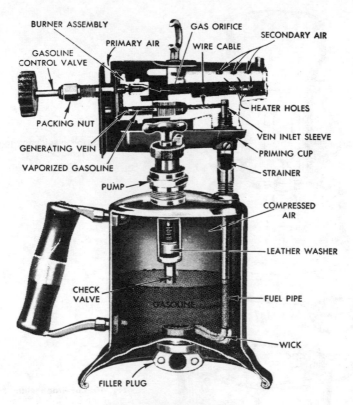

Fig. 43. Gasoline torch.

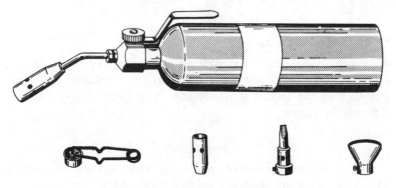

Fig. 44. Propane torch.

187

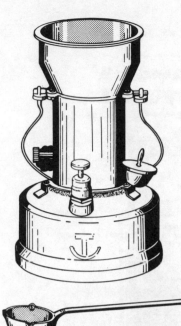

Fig. 45. Gasoline soldering-iron furnace.

Fig. 46. Cast-iron melting pot and ladle.

46). The ladle is used for pouring solder or lead into joints in cast-iron pipes. The best pattern of ladle is provided with three lips so that the melted material can be poured in any of three different directions.

SUMMARY

One of the most common plumbing tools is the pipe wrench. These wrenches are used for turning pipe and fittings, and come in various types, sizes, and lengths. Other useful tools include pipe cutters, reamers, thread dies, and pipe vises.

Flaring tools, tubing cutters, and reamers are useful tools when using copper tubing. These tools can be purchased in several styles and sizes. Hacksaws can also be used for cutting tubing, but special care must be taken to make sure that the cut is made square.

In addition to those tools generally connected with the plumbing trade, the plumber frequently uses tools common to other tradesmen, such as:

Steel measuring tapes.
Chisels.
Levels and plumbs.
Hammers.
Brace and bit.
Portable electric drill.

REVIEW QUESTIONS

1. Why would a twist drill be used when drilling through wood?

2. What is the purpose of a snake rodding line?

3. What is a try square?

4. What is a T-handle tap wrench?

5. What are some of the methods for bending pipe?

CHAPTER 7

Soldering

By definition, *soldering* is the act or process of forming joints upon or between metallic surfaces, by means of a fusible alloy or solder whose melting point is lower than that of the metals sought to be united. Briefly, the process is as follows: After carefully cleaning the joint, a *flux* is applied to prevent oxidation while heated, and a suitable quantity of solder is fused on the joint by a heated copper bit or by a pressure flame, according to whether soft or hard solder is employed. The soft solder easily follows the track of the iron along the heated parts by surface tension, but the hard solder requires more careful preparation and manipulation.

Those who have made a first attempt at soldering will agree that it is an art in itself, and while it looks easy, is not. Moreover, skill cannot be acquired without considerable practice. However, information obtained in books is helpful not only to the beginner, but also to the experienced workman.

SOLDER

The word *solder* is a name for *any fusible alloy used to unite different metal parts*. In electrical work the solder used is usually an alloy of tin and lead. The electrical conductivity of such an alloy is about one-seventh that of copper, so the best joint between copper conductors is made *by bringing the copper surfaces as close together as possible and using a minimum of solder*.

There are two general classes of solder—*soft* and *hard*. Soft solder is composed of lead and tin. Sometimes other metals are

191

added to lower the melting point. Hard solder is composed of copper, zinc, and silver. A relation that must exist between solder and the metal with which it is to unite is that the solder must have a lower melting point than the metals to be joined to it. The melting point should approach as nearly as possible that of the metals to be joined so a more tenacious joint is obtained. Soft solder melts at a low temperature compared to hard solder which melts at a red heat.

Soft Solder

These consist *chiefly of tin and lead,* although other metals are occasionally added to lower the melting point. Those containing the most lead have the highest melting point. According to the tin content, they may be classed as (1) common or plumber's, and (2) medium or fine. Table 1 gives the melting point of tin/lead solder.

Table 1. Melting Points and Hardness of Tin/Lead Solder

Percentage		Approx. Melting	Brinell
Tin	Lead	Temp. Deg. F.	Hardness Test
0	100	620	3.9
10	90	570	10.1
20	80	530	12.16
30	70	501	14.5
40	60	460	15.8
50	50	427	15.0
60	40	370	14.6
70	30	368	15.8
80	20	392	15.2
90	10	421	13.3
100	0	450	4.1

Common or plumber's solder consists of *one part tin to two parts lead, and melts at 441° F*. It is used by plumbers for ordinary work, and occasionally for electrical work where wiped joints are required, for instance, in large lead-covered work. Medium or fine solders consist of equal parts of tin and lead, or *half and half,* and melt at 427° F. This type solder is used for soldering joints in copper conductors, and for soldering lead sleeves on lead-covered wires. In Table 2 will be found the proper solder and flux to use with various metals.

Table 2. Soft Solders and Fluxes for Various Metals

Metal to be Soldered	Flux	PERCENTAGE					
		Tin	Lead	Zinc	Aluminum	Phosphor tin	Bismuth
Aluminum.............	Stearin............................	70		25	3	2	
Brass.................. ⎱	Chloride of zinc, rosin, or ⎰	66	34				
Gun metal......... ⎬	chloride of ammonia.......... ⎨	63	37				
Copper............. ⎰	⎱	60	40				
Lead......................	Tallow or rosin..................	33	67				
Block tin..............	Chloride of zinc..............	99	1				
Tinned steel..........	Chloride of zinc or rosin	64	36				
Galvanized steel...	Hydrochloric acid..............	58	42				
Zinc......................	Hydrochloric Acid..............	55	45				
Pewter..................	Gallipoli oil....................	25	25				50
Iron and steel........	Chloride of ammonia..........	50	50				
Gold......................	Chloride of zinc..............	67	33				
Silver....................	Chloride of zinc..............	67	33				
Bismuth.................	Chloride of zinc.................	33	33				34

Hard Solders

The various solders known as *hard* solders are used for joining such metals as copper, silver, and gold, and such alloys as brass. German silver, gun metal, etc., is required for strong joint, and often a solder with color which is near that of the metal to be joined is used.

Brazing

Brazing is compared with hard soldering. It is generally understood to mean the joining of metals by a filler of brass. A distinguishing characteristic of hard soldering is that a soldering tip cannot be used as in soft soldering because of the excessive temperatures needed. This necessitates the use of a torch, gas forge, or charcoal fire. The chief advantage of a brazed joint is its superior strength. Table 3 gives the various hard solders, proper flux, and metals for which they are suited.

As will be noted from Table 3, most of the hard solders are alloys of copper and zinc. An easily fusible hard solder may be

Table 3. Hard Solders and Fluxes for Various Metals

Metal to be soldered	Flux	PERCENTAGE			
		Copper	Zinc	Silver	Gold
Brass, soft..............................	Borax...................................	22	78		
Brass, hard..............................	Borax...................................	45	55		
Copper....................................	Borax...................................	50	50		
Gold...	Borax...................................	22		11	67
Silver.......................................	Borax...................................	20	10	70	
Cast iron.................................	Cuprous oxide..................	55	45		
Iron and steel........................	Borax...................................	64	36		

made of 1 part copper and 2 parts zinc. This, however, makes a joint that will be weaker than when an alloy more difficult to melt is used. A hard solder that is readily melted is made of 44% copper, 50% zinc, 4% tin, and 2% lead. A hard solder for the richer alloy of copper and zinc may be produced from 53% copper and 47% zinc. When alloys containing much lead are used, the strength of the joint is decreased because lead does not transfuse with brass. The effect of tin is to increase the brittleness of the solder.

MISCELLANEOUS SOLDERS

In addition to the solders already given, there are a number that are of value for various purposes.

Very Hard Yellow Solders

The following formulas make excellent hard solders for all purposes where a high melting point is required:

No. 1. Copper, 58 parts; zinc, 42 parts.
No. 2. Sheet brass, 85.42 parts; zinc, 13.58 parts.
No. 3. Brass, 7 parts; zinc, 1 part.
No. 4. Copper, 53.3 parts; zinc, 43.1 parts; tin, 1.3 parts; lead, 3 parts.

The following four solders have lower melting points, but are more suitable where it is desired to solder only brass.

No. 1. Brass, 66.66 parts; zinc, 33.34 parts.
No. 2. Brass, 50 parts; zinc, 50 parts.
No. 3. Brass, 12 parts; zinc, 4 to 7 parts; tin, 1 part.
No. 4. Copper, 44 parts; zinc, 49 parts; tin, 3.2 parts;
     lead, 1.2 parts.

Silver Solders

These are not, as might be inferred from the name, employed *only* for the purpose of joining silver, but because of their great strength and resistance are used for many other metals. Like all other solders, they may be divided into two groups—soft and hard. Silver solders are usually employed in the shape of wire, narrow strips, or filings. The following are especially adapted to soldering silverware:

Soft Solders

No. 1. Silver, 2 parts; brass, 1 part.
No. 2. Silver, 3 parts; copper, 2 parts; zinc, 1 part.
No. 3. Silver, 10 parts; brass, 10 parts; tin, 1 part.

The following silver solders are suitable for cast iron, steel, and copper:

No. 1. Silver, 10 parts; copper, 10 parts.
No. 2. Silver, 20 parts; copper, 30 parts; zinc, 10 parts.

In addition to the various silver solders already given, two other formulas should be included.

No. 1. Yellow brass, 70 parts; zinc, 7 parts; tin, 11-1/2 parts.
No. 2. Silver, 145 parts; brass (3 copper, 1 zinc), 73 parts;
     zinc, 4 parts.

Hard Solders

No. 1. Copper, 1 part; silver, 4 parts.
No. 2. Copper, 1 part; silver, 20 parts; brass, 9 parts.
No. 3. Copper, 2 parts; silver, 28 parts; brass, 19 parts.

Miscellaneous Silver Solders

Solder for silver-plated work:

No. 1. Fine silver, 2 parts; bronze, 1 part.
No. 2. Silver, 68 parts; copper, 24 parts; zinc, 17 parts.

Solder for silver chains:

No. 1. Fine silver, 74 parts; copper, 24 parts;
orpiment, 2 parts.
No. 2. Fine silver, 40 parts; orpiment, 20 parts;
copper, 40 parts.

Resoldering silver solders: These silver solders are for resoldering parts already soldered.

No. 1. Silver, 3 parts; copper, 2 parts; zinc, 1 part.
No. 2. Silver, 1 part; brass, 1 part; or silver, 7 parts;
copper, 3 parts; zinc, 2 parts.

Fusible silver solder for ordinary work:

Silver, 5 parts; copper, 6 parts; zinc, 2 parts.

German-Silver Solders

German silver is a very hard alloy of copper (50% to 60%), nickel (15% to 25%), and zinc (15% to 20%). German silver containing 1% to 2% of tungsten is called *platinoid*. These alloys have a high electrical resistance, platinoid being higher than the other varieties of German silver; the resistance increases uniformly between 32° and 212° F. German-silver solders possess considerable strength, and are often used for soldering steel, the color being very similar to that of steel. In preparing German-silver solders, the copper is melted first, and then the zinc and nickel added simultaneously.

Soft German-Silver Solders

No. 1. Copper, 4.5 parts; zinc, 7 parts; nickel, 1 part.
No. 2. Copper, 35 parts; zinc, 56.5 parts; nickel, 8.5 parts.
No. 3. Copper, 38 parts; zinc, 54 parts; nickel, 8 parts.

Hard German-Silver Solders

These solders, sometimes called steel solders, contain a large proportion of nickel and are very strong. They require a very high heat for melting, and usually cannot be fused without the aid of a bellows or blast.

No. 1. Copper, 35 parts; zinc, 56.5 parts; nickel 9.5 parts.
No. 2. Copper, 38 parts; zinc, 50 parts; nickel, 12 parts.

In soldering German-silver articles, the solder is usually applied in the form of a powder or in very small pieces or lumps. The solder may be powdered in a mortar if taken from the fire at the right temperature when it is brittle. This operation is a somewhat difficult one, and so the usual, and perhaps the best, plan is to cast it in the form of a bar or cylinder and then place the latter in a turning lathe and adjust the tool so that fine shavings are cut off. The shavings are then heated until they become brittle, at which stage they are easily pulverized in a mortar.

Aluminum Solders

In soldering aluminum, it is necessary to tin the parts that are to be soldered. This tinning is done with the iron, using a composition of aluminum and tin. A pure aluminum soldering bit should be used. To prepare an aluminum solder, first melt the copper, then add the aluminum gradually, and stir well with an iron rod; next add the zinc and a little tallow or benzine at the same time. After adding the zinc, do not heat too quickly.

SOLDERING FLUXES

The word *flux* means a *substance applied to a metal to make solder flow readily on its surface*. The action of a flux is to clean the surface, and to reduce any oxide on the surface to the metallic state. If a piece of sheet copper is carefully cleaned by means of emery cloth and heated over a gas flame, the surface will be seen to tarnish rapidly and assume a dark-brown appearance. A small piece of rosin dropped on the surface will melt, and when the liquid runs, the initial brightness of the surface will be found to reappear. There are a number of fluxes suitable for various kinds of soldering, but pine amber rosin is good for electrical work as it does not cause corrosion. A corrosive flux, such as zinc-chloride solution (killed spirits) should be excluded from electrical work. The nature of the solder often determines the flux. Table 4 will serve as a guide in the selection of the ordinary fluxes.

Table 4. Selection of Solder Flux

Metals to be soldered	Flux	Metals to be soldered	Flux
Iron	Borax	Zinc	Chloride of zinc
Tinned iron	Rosin	Lead	Tallow or rosin
Copper and brass	Sal-ammoniac	Lead and tin	Rosin and sweet oil

Rosin

This substance is difficult to define. It is undoubtedly an exudation from the trunk and limbs of trees, but these exudations vary so much in all properties that the terminology of them is wide, complicated, and, in some cases, contradictory. Rosin solidifies after exudation from the tree and is insoluble in water but soluble in alcohol. Colophony is the kind used as a flux, and consists of other coagulated exudation obtained from cuts in the bark of trees belonging to several species of Pinus, largely grown in America and on the west coast of France. It comes in lumps, but can be granulated by grinding or simply by hammering. The rosin may be sprinkled over the surface to be soldered or may be applied in liquid form by dissolving in alcohol. It is used as a flux for brass, copper, gun metal, lead, and tinned steel.

Chloride of Zinc

This flux, which may be used for brass, copper, gun metal, block tin, tinned steel, gold, silver, and bismuth, is prepared as follows: Place 3 parts of hydrochloric (muriatic) acid and 1 part of water in a glass, wooden, or lead vessel, and add pieces of zinc as long as the acid attacks the zinc. Put in the zinc gradually to prevent boiling over. Care should be taken to get a saturated solution; that is, to add all the zinc that the solution will dissolve. After settling, the clear solution should be poured off and the latter is then ready for use. Another flux made with zinc chloride that is especially adapted to the soft soldering of iron and steel (because it does not make rust spots) consists of the ordinary zinc chloride with the addition of one-third part spirits of sal-ammoniac and one-third part rain water; the mixture is filtered before using.

A formula which dispenses with the use of chloride of zinc consists of: water, 80%; lactic acid, 10%; glycerine, 10%. An acid-free soldering fluid consists of: 5 parts chloride of zinc, 25 parts of boiling water. Another: 20 parts chloride of zinc, 10 parts ammoniac chloride; 100 parts boiling water. Another formula consists of chloride of zinc, 1 dram; alcohol, 1 ounce.

Rosin and Tallow

A mixture commonly used consists of rosin and tallow with the addition of a small quantity of sal-ammoniac. This is adapted to tinned ware because of the ease with which it may be wiped off the surface after soldering. Another mixture consists of: 1-1/2 lbs. olive oil; 1-1/2 lbs. tallow; 12 oz. pulverized rosin. Let the mixture boil and, when cool, add 1-3/8 pints of water saturated with pulverized sal-ammoniac, stirring constantly.

Soldering Grease

In a pot of sufficient size and using a slow fire, melt together 500 parts of olive oil and 400 parts of tallow, then stir in slowly 250 parts of rosin powder, and let the mixture boil once. After cooling, add 125 parts of saturated solution of sal-ammoniac while stirring; use when cold.

Ammonia Soap

Mix fine powdered rosin with a strong ammonia solution. This is suitable for soldering copper wires for electrical conduits.

Soldering Fat for Iron

Olive oil, 50 parts; sal-ammoniac, 50 parts.

199

Soldering Fat for Aluminum

Melt together equal parts of rosin and tallow, adding one-half part of chloride of zinc to the mixture.

Soldering Salt

Mix equal parts of neutral chloride of zinc, free from acid, and powdered sal-ammoniac. When required for use, 1 part of the salt should be dissolved in 3 or 4 parts of water.

Soldering Paste

Soldering paste consists of neutral soldering liquid thickened with starch paste. In using, apply more lightly than the soldering liquid.

Borax

This flux is most frequently used for hard soldering. It should be applied to the soldering seam either dry or stirred to a paste with water. It is advisable to use borax which has been dried by heat (calcined borax). For soldering steel on steel, or iron on steel, melt in an earthen vessel: borax, 3 parts; colophony, 2 parts; pulverized glass, 3 parts; steel filings, 2 parts; carbonate of potash, 1 part; hard-soap powder, 1 part. Flow the melted mass on a cold plate of sheet iron, and after cooling, break up the pieces and pulverize them. This powder is thrown on the surfaces a few minutes before the pieces to be soldered are brought together. The borax and glass dissolve, liquefying all impurities, which, if they were shut up between the pieces soldered, might form scales.

Cryolite

Fine powdered cryolite is suitable for hard soldering of copper and copper alloys, or a mixture of 2 parts powdered cryolite, and 1 part phosphoric acid may be used. For hard soldering of aluminum bronze, a mixture of equal parts of cryolite and barium chloride is used.

Dry Soldering Preparation

A good preparation consists of two vials, one filled with chloride of zinc and the other with ammonium chloride. To use, dissolve a little of each in salt water, apply the ammonium chloride to the object to be soldered and heat the latter until it begins to give off vapors of ammonium, then apply the other, maintaining the heat in the meantime. This will work for very soft solder; for a harder solder, dissolve the zinc in a very small portion of the ammonium chloride solution (from 1/4 to 1/2 pint).

SOLDERING BOLTS OR BITS

The soldering "iron" or bit consists of a large piece of copper, drawn to a point or edge and fastened to an iron rod having a wooden handle, as shown in Fig. 1. There is a variety of tips which may be classed with respect to their shape or construction as:

Fig. 1. An electric hand soldering iron.

1. Diamond.
2. Chisel.
3. Screwdriver.
4. Cone.
5. Turned down.

The various types of tips are shown in Fig. 2.

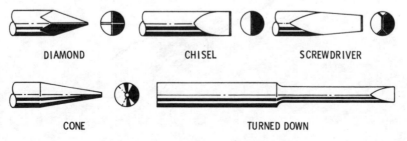

DIAMOND   CHISEL   SCREWDRIVER

CONE   TURNED DOWN

Fig. 2. Various replaceable soldering-iron tips.

201

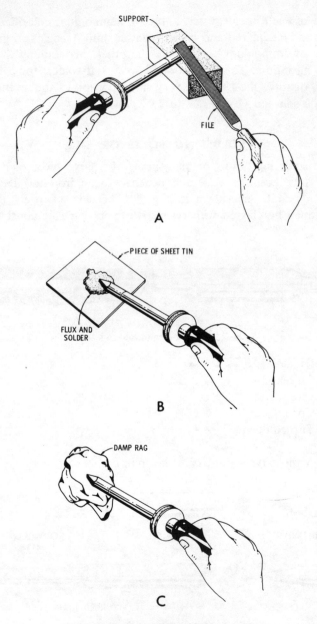

Fig. 3. Method of tinning soldering-iron tip.

Tinning the Tip

Preliminary to soldering, the tip must be coated with solder, this operation being known as *tinning*. To tin a soldering tip, the iron must be hot enough to melt solder rapidly when it is lightly pressed against the solder surface. When the tip is at the right temperature, the heat can be felt when it is held close to the face. When hot enough, clean the surface of the copper with a file.

If the temperature is too high, the copper surface will be found to tarnish immediately, in which case the soldering tip must be allowed to cool slightly and the cleaning repeated. When the surface tarnishes slowly, a little flux is sprinkled on it and is then rubbed with a stick of solder. After the molten metal has spread over the entire surface of the tip, the superfluous solder is wiped off with a clean damp rag. The surface should then present a bright silvery appearance when properly tinned.

The operation of tinning the tip is shown in Fig. 3. Once a soldering tip has been well tinned, care should be taken not to overheat it. If the tip at any time reaches a red heat, it will be necessary to repeat the whole tinning process before it is fit to be used again. Good work cannot be done with an untinned or badly tinned tip. If the tip is forgotten and left in the fire, heat to redness and then plunge into cold water; most of the hard oxidized surface will scale off. A hot fire will quickly destroy the tinning.

SOFT SOLDERING

The theory of soft soldering is that as the solder adheres to and unites with the surface of the copper when the tip is tinned, so will it adhere to and unite the surfaces of the metal to be soldered. Soft soldering, as well as hard soldering or brazing, consists of uniting two or more pieces of similar or dissimilar metals by means of another metal of lower melting point.

In order to solder wire joints successfully, the following instructions should be followed:

1. Clean and tin the tip.

2. Heat the tip in the fire until it reaches the right temperature. Do not try to solder a joint with a tip so cool that it only

melts the solder slowly, nor with one so hot that it gives dense clouds of smoke when in contact with rosin. Burned rosin must be regarded as dirt.

3. Remove the tip from the fire and hold it, or preferably support it, on a brick or block of other material which does not conduct heat readily.

4. Wipe the surface clean with a rag. Apply solder until a pool remains on the flat surface, or in the groove, if a grooved tip is used.

5. Sprinkle with rosin, lay the joint in the pool of solder, and again sprinkle with rosin.

6. Rub the joint with a stick of solder so that every crevice is thoroughly filled.

7. Remove the tip and lightly brush the superfluous solder from the bottom of the joint. See that no sharp points of solder remain which may afterwards pierce the insulation.

When the joint is first placed on the tip, the solder should run up into the joint. This will occur only when the joint is well made and thoroughly cleaned, and if the workmanship is perfect, it is possible to fill the joint completely by feeding in solder below the joint as it melts and runs up into the joint. A well-soldered joint should present a smooth, bright appearance like polished silver. Wiping the joint before it cools destroys this appearance, and is also liable to produce roughness, which is detrimental to the insulation.

SOLDERING WITH A TORCH

The flame is directed on the middle of the joint, and when a sufficient rise of temperature has taken place to melt the solder readily, the joint is rubbed with rosin and solder alternately until it is thoroughly saturated with solder. The usual precaution of brushing any points of solder off the joint with a clean rag must, of course, be taken.

In using the torch, there is considerable danger of damaging the insulation with the flame. This may be minimized by wrapping the end of the insulation with selvage tape before soldering. When big joints are being made, it is sometimes advisable to wet the tape in order to prevent the conduction of heat along the copper to the insulation.

SWEATING

In this operation *the surfaces are cleaned, heated, and covered with a film of solder.* The soldered surfaces are then placed together and heated by passing the tip over the outside surface until the solder melts and unites the two surfaces. Sweating is often employed for the temporary holding together of work which has to be turned or shaped, and which could not be so conveniently held by other methods. After having been turned or shaped, the separation of the parts is readily effected by the aid of heat.

LEAD BURNING

This process, sometimes called autogenous soldering, consists of *joining pieces of lead together by simply placing the edges to be joined close to or overlapping each other, and then melting them so that they flow and intermingle with each other, forming one piece and retaining the same condition of unison on solidifying.* In some cases, a strip of lead is melted at the same time as the edges; this makes a raised and, consequently, a stronger seam. The process is useful only for joining lead to lead and would not answer so well for joining lead to copper or to brass. In lead burning, a hydrogen flame is used in connection with a jet of air, the hydrogen being produced in a machine or generator, or purchased in tanks.

For joining lead sheets together by burning, it is essential that the pieces touch or overlap each other when in the horizontal position, and overlap when in either slanting, upright, or overhead positions. It is not necessary to soil the sides of the seams, because the lead will flow only where it is directed by the flame jet. No fluxes are necessary.

205

If the flame tarnishes or smokes the lead stick, more air or oxygen should be used. If the lead turns to a silvery brightness when the flame strikes it, the heat will be right and the part of the flame to be used will be ascertained. During the process of burning, the sheet lead will expand when the heat is applied, and being a poor conductor, the heat is not distributed to the adjoining sides of the seam; hence, the heated parts will rise up and leave hollow spaces underneath. When this happens, it leaves places where the lead does not join together and the lead melts more readily, resulting in a hole through which the molten metal will flow.

SOLDERING COPPER TUBING AND PIPING

From the earliest development of soldered fittings and their many applications, an extensive research program has been conducted to determine the solder alloys having the most desirable physical properties. As most of the uses of copper water tube and soldered fittings are concerned with moderate temperatures and pressures, *soft* solders have been considered as having adequate physical properties. *Soft* solders are commonly referred to as those alloys which have melting temperatures below 600°F. Among the great number of alloys tested with melting temperatures within this range, many were found which had some very desirable properties but were noticeably lacking in others. Of those tested, the solder having the desired qualities was an alloy of 95% tin and 5% antimony. Common solder alloys in this temperature range are 50% tin-50% lead, or 40% tin-60% lead.

The choice of the proper flux to use with soft solders is of great importance. The primary function of a flux for this purpose is to chemically clean the surfaces of the tube and fitting after they have been mechanically cleaned by the use of an abrasive material such as steel wool or sand cloth. As metals have a tendency to oxidize more rapidly when heated, another purpose of the flux is to prevent oxidation. This allows the solder to flow freely and form a good bond within the joint. Although a flux must be corrosive to some extent to perform these functions, the degree of corrosiveness should be such that the fluxing action itself renders

the flux almost chemically inert and protects the thin film of solde ·
within the joint against further corrosive attack. Precleaning is
necessary, because such fluxes may be corrosive to such an extent that the complete joint may be subject to corrosive attack
over a long period of time. The most commonly available fluxes
best adapted to the joining of soldered fittings and copper water
tube are compounds of relatively mild concentrations of zinc and
ammonium chlorides mixed with a petrolatum carrier. These fluxes
will form good sound soldered joint connections when the proper
procedure is followed.

The use of the term *hard* solders usually designates solder
alloys which have melting temperatures exceeding 600°F. Most
all hard solders in common use, however, have melting temperatures considerably higher than this, and melt at temperatures in
excess of 1100°F. These alloys are also known (depending on
their composition) as silver solders, silver-type solders, or low-
temperature brazing alloys. Where piping systems are subjected
to fairly high temperatures or pressures, or unusual stresses are to
be considered, hard solders are generally recommended. The
properties most desired in such a solder include good flowing and
joint penetration, high strength with relatively low melting points,
and a cost per pound that would not be excessive. Although
many of the high silver content solders have the desired characteristics, they are expensive. There are several readily available
alloys which fill all requirements at reasonable cost. Some of
these are *Sil-Fos* and *Easy-Flo,* manufactured by Handy & Har-
man, Inc. of New York City; *Phos-Copper,* manufactured by
Westinghouse Electric Corporation of Wilmerding, Pa.; and *Pho-
son,* manufactured by United Wire & Supply Corp. of Providence,
R. I.

Because of the composition of the alloys named above, they
can be used without a flux provided the tube and fitting surfaces
are clean. Any of these solders, however, will *wet* the fitting and
tube surfaces more readily, flow better, and give better penetration
when a flux is used. There are a number of good prepared flux
compounds available for this type of solder. A satisfactory flux
may be made by mixing powdered borax and alcohol or water to
this milky solution. When painted on with a small brush, it will

leave a thin film which is ample for good soldering. Care must be taken not to use excessive quantities of flux in this soldering operation, as the flux may load up on the joint and cause uneven distribution of the solder. Also, the flux may fillet in the same manner as the solder, contributing to faulty joints. Melted solder is drawn into a soldered fitting by capillary action much as ink is drawn into a blotter. To assure this action, it is necessary that the space tolerances between the tube and the fitting be very closely controlled.

HARD-SOLDER JOINTS FOR COPPER TUBING

Hard solders do not penetrate the full depth of the joint as easily as soft solders. Because of their higher physical strengths, it is not necessary to have more than a nominal penetration, providing a uniform light fillet is formed at the edge of the joint. The high temperatures necessary to cause these hard solders to flow will anneal the tube at or near the joint. A well-filleted joint will be stronger than the tube at this point. Although a blow-torch or air-gas torch may be used in making hard solder joints up to 1″ or 1-1/4″ in size, oxyacetylene equipment is recommended for larger sizes.

To make a hard-solder joint in copper piping and fittings, the tube and fitting surfaces need not be polished brightly as is necessary for a soft-solder joint, but they must be free of oxides or stains. No. 00 steel wool or sand cloth may be used. A very thin film of solder flux or other low-temperature brazing flux should be applied to the tube and fitting surfaces. A small brush will best serve this purpose. After the fitting is placed on the tube, remove any excess flux that shows outside the joint other than a thin coating.

The flame should be played over the entire joint until it is uniformly heated to a dull red. This applies to fittings up to 1″ only. With larger diameter fittings, a 1″ or 2″ arc of the joint circumference should be heated to a dull red after the torch is first applied to all joint and adjacent fitting surfaces in preheating. As the temperature of an oxycetylene flame is very high, it must be held slightly away from the joint and kept in motion to prevent burning the flux or spot melting the fitting. The hard-solder wire is then applied to the edge of the joint. Underheating has a tendency to cause the solder to *ball* or load up at one point and improperly wet the joint surfaces. Overheating, before applying the solder, will burn the flux and create excessive oxidation, making it very difficult to wet the joint surfaces. Excessive over-heating of cast fittings may cause cracking. Excessive heating may also cause the lead in the alloy to come to the surface, making it extremely difficult for the solder to flow or adhere.

It is further suggested that a *soft* or lower pressure flame be used to prevent wasteful spreading of the solder. To get good penetration of the joint, move the flame back over the area toward the shoulder of the fitting and, when the solder ceases to flow into the joint, a smooth fillet of solder should be formed at the edge of the fitting. This process should be followed around the edge of the joint until a complete and uniform fillet is obtained. The joint should then be permitted to cool. Although copper fittings may be quickly chilled, cast-brass fittings must cool slowly in air to minimize thermal stresses.

CUTTING COPPER TUBE

In the preparation of the tube for soft- or hard-soldered con-nections, it is recommended the tube be cut square. If a hacksaw is used, a 24- or 32-tooth blade is preferred. Miter tools are avail-able for sizes up to 2 inches. In sawing large-diameter tubes a template, a straight-edge piece of sheet metal, or stiff paper may be used to mark a line to guide the saw cut. Use a half-round file to remove the burrs from the outside and inside edges of the tube. Rounding or chamfering the edges of a large-diameter tube will make it easier to insert the tube into the sleeve of the fitting.

SOLDER-JOINT VALVES

Plumbing, heating, and air-conditioning systems require sturdy valves with resistant features. *Kennedy* valves, with cylindrical-shaped bodies, have excellent distortion-resisting qualities, and the stem design assures maximum resistance to the common cause of

Fig. 4. A typical solder-end bronze
gate valve.

stem failure. Solder joints have threadless, smooth pipe ends, into
which standard types of copper tubing can be fitted. At the inner
end of the socket, a square shoulder acts as a stop which limits
pipe insertion (see Fig. 4).

Caution: The safe working pressure-temperature ratings for a
soldered piping system are dependent not only on the valves and
tube strength, but also on the composition of the solder used for
joints. Do not use a solder-joint valve on lines carrying flammable
gases or liquids. In the event of fire, heat might melt the solder
joint, releasing the liquid or gas as additional fuel for the flames.
Also, a pipe fitter attempting to dismantle a solder joint on a gas
line by melting out the joints might cause a fire or explosion
from the residue of oil or gas in the line.

When solder-joint valves are installed, the type of solder used
must be suitable for the service pressure and temperature. Solder-
joint valves must be open when installed.

SUMMARY

Soldering employs lead- or tin-base alloys with melting points
below 600°F, and is commonly referred to as soft solder. Use of
hard solders, silver solders, and spelter solders which have silver,
copper, or nickel bases and melting points above 600°F, is known
as brazing. Soldering is used to provide a convenient joint that
does not require any great mechanical strength.

Soft solders can be obtained in bar, cake, wire, slab, powder,
and foil form for various uses. In bar form, it is commonly used

for hand soldering. The pigs, ingots, and slab form is used in operations that employ melting kettles or pots. Wire forms are either solid or they can contain acid or rosin cores for fluxing. The wire form is usually used in hand and automatic machine applications.

The surfaces of the metals being joined in the soldering operation must be clean in order to obtain an efficient joint. Fluxes clean the surfaces of the metal in the joint area by removing the oxide coating present, keep the area clean by preventing formation of oxide films, and lower the surface tension of the solder, thereby increasing its wetting properties.

REVIEW QUESTIONS

1. What is the purpose of fluxing the metal to be soldered?

2. Should hard solder or soft solder be used in connecting copper tubing and fittings?

3. Why is rosin-core solder used in electrical work?

4. What is the purpose of sweat connections?

5. What happens if a soldering iron is not tinned?

CHAPTER 8

Lead Work

Although lead pipe has been largely replaced by brass and steel pipe, the plumber should have a knowledge of lead work. To wipe a joint and make a good job of it requires a knowledge of the principles involved and considerable practice.

JUDGING THE SOLDER

A requirement in lead work is the ability to judge the quality of solder. The plumber must know by its appearance when it contains the right proportions of lead and tin. To preserve these proportions, it is necessary to keep the solder from overheating, because in overheating, some of the tin will burn, thus destroying the correct proportions. The tin burns because its melting point is lower than that of the lead. The quality of the solder may be judged by pouring out a small quantity on a brick or stone and noting the color when it sets, also the number and size of bright spots on its surface. When the proportions are correct, there will appear on a test sample (almost the size of a half dollar) about four small bright spots. The side of the solder next to the brick will be bright. Adding lead will reduce the size and number of spots; adding tin increases them. Thoroughly stir the solder before pouring out a test sample. The rate of cooling affects the appearance of the test sample; if cooled too quickly, the solder will appear *finer* than it really is.

When the tin burns, it is indicated by the formation of dross on the surface, specks of which turn bright red and smoke. Too

213

little tin in the solder will cause the solder to melt the lead pipe on which it is poured; it will burn the tinning of a brass ferrule or union and set free zinc from the brass which will mix with the solder and render it unfit for joint wiping. The right heat of the solder is judged by the color or bloom on the surface of the molten solder, or by holding the ladle near the face. An easier test for the beginner is to stir with a wooden stick; when it is at the right temperature it will char the stick, and if too hot, the stick will burn.

PROPORTIONING THE SOLDER

Ordinarily, solder is made with twice as much lead as tin. In using solder, the numerous heatings and occasional overheating will result in losing some of the tin by burning. It is necessary to add a little tin to the solder from time to time to make up this loss. Since the tin is lighter than the lead, it tends to float on top of the lead. Hence, unless the solder is stirred before dipping the ladle, an excess amount of tin will be removed. These two causes for the loss of tin are emphasized in Table 1.

Table 1. Properties of Lead and Tin

Ingredients	Melting Point	Specific Gravity	Weight	
			Per cu. in.	Per cu. ft.
Lead	620°F.	11.07 to 11.44	.4106	709.7
Tin	449°F.	7.297 to 7.409	.2652	458.3

Solder composed of 2 parts lead and 1 part tin is called plumbers' solder, and is suitable for wiping joints. The following method of making plumbers' solder is recommended:

Use 100 lbs. of good old lead or lead cuttings, melt it down thoroughly, stir it up and take off all dirt or dross. Take 50 lbs. of pure tin, let this melt down, and when nearly all is melted and is slightly cooled, throw in 1/2 lb. of black rosin and stir well. Heat to 600°F, which may be determined if a piece of newspaper put in the pot ignites. The solder is now hot enough and should be well stirred and then put into molds. Solder at this point will melt at 440°F.

CLEANING SOLDER

In using solder, it is frequently rendered unfit by:

1. Overheating.
2. Falling unprotected and picking up foreign matter.

Overheating, as already explained, causes loss of tin by burning, thus destroying the correct proportion of tin to lead. In the process of pouring solder in joint wiping, a certain amount falls from the joint. If this falls, say on a bench where it may mechanically pick up zinc or brass filings and is returned to the pot, the entire contents of the pot will be rendered unfit for use until the zinc has been removed and the solder brought back to the correct porportions. In order to get rid of the zinc, it is necessary to heat the solder to 773°F, which is the melting point of zinc. The zinc, being lighter than either lead or tin, will melt and rise to the top and can then be skimmed off.

When the zinc solder has been heated sufficiently to melt the zinc, throw in a lump of sulfur or rosin and stir, which will increase its buoyancy. The top will then consist of a mixture of lead oxide, putty powder, sulfur, and zinc. Let cool to a working point and stir in some tallow and rosin and again skim. The tin lost by overheating to remove the zinc should be replaced with more tin. In removing zinc, be careful not to heat the solder any more than necessary; never let the solder become "red hot" in daylight.

PREPARING JOINT FOR WIPING

It is important that the ends of the lead pipes to be joined are properly treated before wiping. The two essential requirements for a satisfactory flow of liquid through the pipe in service are as follows:

1. That the ends of the pipes to be joined properly fit so that, in pouring the solder, it will not run through the joint and form an obstruction.
2. That there are no sharp internal projections at the joint which would catch lint or any other foreign matter.

In addition, the formation given to the ends of the pipes should be such as to form a socket into which the solder will flow, thus making the joint stronger than if merely built up around the outer surfaces of the two pipes.

The operations to be performed in preparing the joint for wiping consists of:

1. Squaring.
2. Removing burrs.
3. Flaring the female end.
4. Rasping the outer edge.
5. Pointing the male end.
6. Soiling.
7. Marking.
8. Shaving.
9. Setting.

Various tools are used in performing these operations.

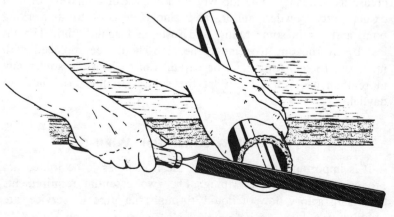

Fig. 1. Preparing a joint for wiping by squaring the end.

To secure a good fitting joint, so that when the solder is poured it will not run inside the pipes, the ends of the pipe must first be squared, as shown in Fig. 1. Cut the pipe as true as possible. The skilled workman will be able to judge when the end is square "by eye," but the beginner should use a try square to test the trueness of the end. When the pipe is cut, especially if a wheel

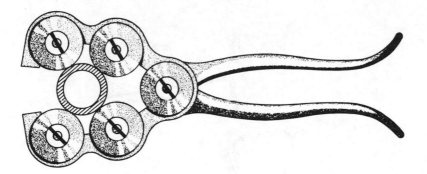

Fig. 2. Wheel lead-pipe cutter.

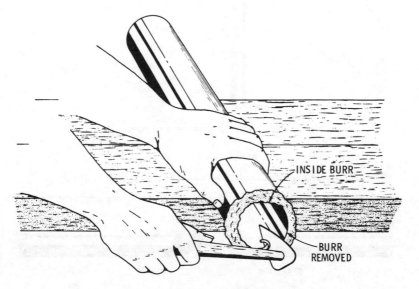

Fig. 3. Removing burrs from end of pipe.

217

cutter is used (such as shown in Fig. 2), burrs will be formed on the inside and outside of the pipe. At this stage, the inside burr should be removed by using a reamer, tap borer, or a shave hook, as shown in Fig. 3.

In the further preparation of the ends, the *female end* is flared or belled out with a *turn pin* as shown in Fig. 4. The pipe is flared so that the end is enlarged about a quarter of an inch. This oper-

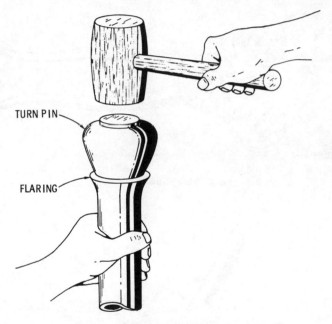

TURN PIN

FLARING

Fig. 4. Flaring female end of pipe.

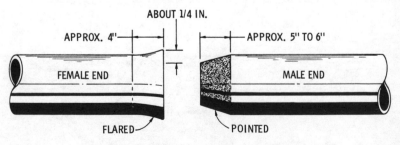

ABOUT 1/4 IN.

APPROX. 4"

APPROX. 5" TO 6"

FEMALE END

MALE END

FLARED

POINTED

Fig. 5. Shape of female and male ends of lead pipe.

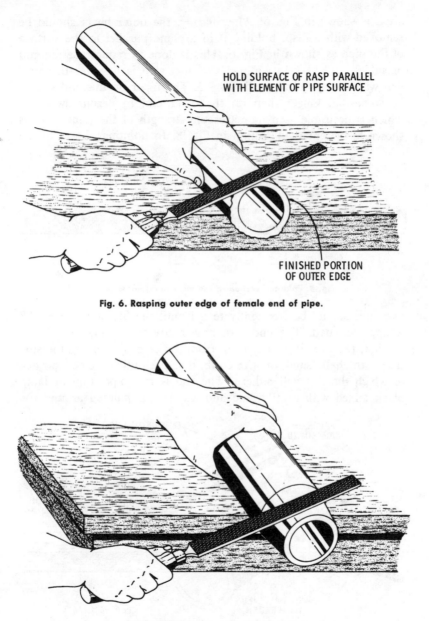

HOLD SURFACE OF RASP PARALLEL
WITH ELEMENT OF PIPE SURFACE

FINISHED PORTION
OF OUTER EDGE

Fig. 6. Rasping outer edge of female end of pipe.

Fig. 7. Pointing the male end of pipe.

ation is shown in Fig. 5. After flaring, the outer burrs should be removed with a rasp, holding it in a plane parallel to the surface of the pipe as shown in Fig. 6. This is done to reduce the amount of solder necessary in wiping. The next step is to *point* the *male end* with a rasp, as shown in Fig. 7. The taper on this end should be somewhat longer than on the other end to permit sweating, which is desirable as it increases the strength of the joint. This is shown in the enlarged section in Fig. 8. In pointing, the fit of the

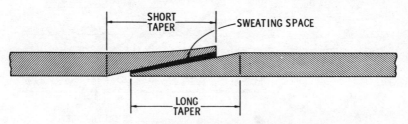

SHORT TAPER — SWEATING SPACE

LONG TAPER

Fig. 8. Enlarged section of the male and female pipe.

two ends should be frequently tested until the fit shown in Fig. 8 is approximated. The ends are now ready for soiling.

First, remove all grease or oil from the pipe by rubbing the surface with chalk, sand, or wire cloth, thus presenting a clean surface to which the soil will adhere. The soil is a composition of lamp black mixed with a little glue and water; it is painted around the

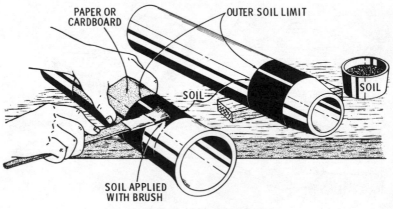

PAPER OR CARDBOARD

OUTER SOIL LIMIT

SOIL

SOIL

SOIL APPLIED WITH BRUSH

Fig. 9. Applying the soil to the pipe.

pipe (as shown in Fig. 9) to prevent the adhesion of the melted solder except at its proper place, thus giving a neat and finished appearance. Plumbers' soil ready to mix with cold water may be obtained from dealers. In the absence of the prepared article, use old-fashioned shoe blacking; this, however, is not as satisfactory as regular soil. To make the soil, take 1/2 oz. of pulverized glue and dissolve it in water, and gradually add a pint of dry lamp black with water enough to bring it to the consistency of cream. Boil and stir until the glue is thoroughly incorporated with the black. This will have to be done slowly, and when it has progressed far enough, test it as follows. Paint a little of the soil on a piece of pipe and, when dry, rub it smartly with your finger. If it comes off easily, add more glue, but if it sticks and takes a slight polish, it is good. If it curls off when heat is applied, there is too much glue in it, or the pipe was not cleaned previous to applying.

The entire end of each pipe is painted, with the soil extending beyond the joint limit as shown in Fig. 9. The neat workman will paint the outer soil limit (on both pipes) to the lines by wrapping a piece of paper or cardboard around the pipe with the edge at the desired outer soil limit. After the soil dries, the excess must be removed from the pipe end up to the inner soil limit, which governs the length of the joint or the distance along the pipe to which the solder will adhere. The pipe ends are now ready for *shaving*. This consists of removing the soil between the pipe end and the inner soil limit in order to obtain a clean bright surface

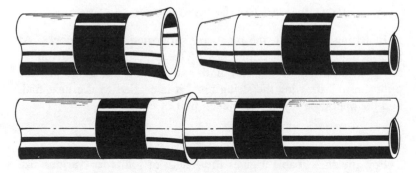

Fig. 10. Soil applied to pipe ends for joint wiping.

221

to which the solder will adhere. Both the internal and external surfaces must be shaved so that all the surface which should come in contact with the solder will be bright, otherwise the solder will not adhere.

Immediately after shaving, apply a little tallow to the shaved surfaces to preserve them from the oxidizing action of the atmosphere, which would otherwise tarnish the surface and form a film to which the solder will not adhere. The pipes are now ready for the final preparatory operation of setting. They have the appearance shown in Fig. 10.

Setting the pipes or fixing them rigidly in position so they will not move during the wiping operation often taxes the ingenuity of the workman. It is an easy job on the bench, but in a building, between beams or in other cramped places, it is often very difficult to get proper support and leave room for manipulating the solder. In bench work, the pipe may be set either with blocks and string, or with clamps.

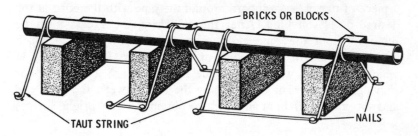

Fig. 11. Supporting lead pipe in preparing joint for wiping.

In setting (Fig. 11), the pipes are supported on four blocks. At intermediate points on both sides of the pipe, nails are driven. A string is attached to the end nail and a turn taken around the opposite nail drawing the string taut; it is carried to the next nail, and the operation repeated for each pair of nails.

LENGTH OF JOINT

For guidance, Table 2 gives the length of joints for various size pipes. The lengths specified in Table 2 represent the average

American practice and will be found amply large for strength and durability, and the proportions give a pleasing appearance. The table also gives the size of wiping cloths.

Table 2. Lengths of Wiped Joints

Pipe diameter (inches)	One-hand system		Two-hand system	
	Length of joint (inches)	Size of cloth (inches)	Length of joint (inches)	Size of cloth (inches)
½	2	3 × 3	2¼	3 × 4
¾	2	3 × 3	2⅜	3 × 4
1	2	3 × 3	2⅜	3 × 4
1¼ water	2	3 × 3	2½	3¼ × 4
1¼ waste	2	3 × 3	2⅜	3 × 4
1½ water	2	3 × 3	2½	3¼ × 4
1½ waste	2	3 × 3	2⅜	3 × 4
2 waste	2	3 × 3	2⅜	3¼ × 4
3 waste	2	3 × 3	2½	3¼ × 4
4 waste	1¾	3 × 3, 6 × 6	2¾	3¼ × 4, 3¼ × 5
2 vertical	1¾	3 × 3	2	3 × 2½
3 vertical	1¾	3 × 3	2	3 × 2½
4 vertical	1¾	3 × 3	2	3 × 2½

WIPING THE JOINT

After the pipe ends have been prepared, as just described, they are ready for the final operation of wiping. The tools needed are the furnace pot (Fig. 12) and ladle (Fig. 13) for melting and dipping out the lead, and a wiping cloth. The following information in Table 3 gives the amount of solder required for wiping joints of various sizes of pipe.

For joints up to 2 inches in diameter, a pot containing 10 lbs. of solder will ordinarily be large enough.

There are three methods of wiping:

Fig. 12. Illustrating a typical melting pot.

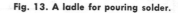

Fig. 13. A ladle for pouring solder.

Table 3. Solder Required for Wiped Joints

Size of Pipe (inches)	½	¾	1	1¼	1¼ water	1½ waste
Ounces of Solder	9	12	16	16	18	18

Size of Pipe (inches)	1½ water	2 waste	3 waste	4 waste	4 vertical
Ounces of Solder	20	20	24	34	28

1. One-hand.
2. Two-hand.
3. Rolling method.

On making a joint by the one-hand method, a quantity of solder is taken from the pot by means of the ladle, the solder being previously heated so hot that the hand cannot be held closer than two inches from the surface. The solder is poured lightly on the joint, the ladle being moved backward and forward, so that too much solder is not put in one place. The solder is also poured an inch or two on the soiling, to make the pipe the proper temperature. Naturally, the further the heat is run or taken along the pipe, the

224

better the chance of making the joint. The operator keeps pouring, and with his left hand holds the cloth to catch the solder and to tin the lower side of the pipe, and also to keep the solder from dripping down. By the process of steady pouring, the solder now becomes soft and begins to feel shaped, firm, and bulky.

When in this shape and in a semifluid condition the ladle is put down and, with the left hand, the operation of wiping (Fig. 14) is

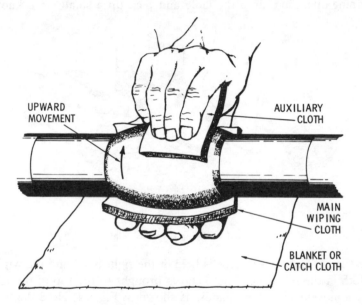

UPWARD
MOVEMENT

AUXILIARY
CLOTH

MAIN
WIPING
CLOTH

BLANKET OR
CATCH CLOTH

Fig. 14. Wiping a horizontal joint.

begun, working from the soiling toward the top of the bulb. If the lead cools rapidly, it is reheated to a plastic condition by a torch or a heated iron. When the joint is completed, it is cooled with a water spray so that the lead does not have time to alter its shape. The cloth used for wiping is a pad of moleskin or fustian about four inches square made from a piece of 9×12 inch material, folded six times and sewed to keep it from opening. The side next to the pipe is saturated with hot tallow when used. If the lead has been brought to the heat of the solder, and the latter properly manipulated and shaped while in a semifluid or plastic

225

condition, the joint gradually assumes the finished egg-shaped appearance.

In wiping a vertical joint, a small piece of cardboard is placed under the joint to catch excess solder, as shown in Fig. 15, forming a flange held in place around the pipe by twine. In wiping by the two-hand method, as soon as there is a sufficient body of solder around the pipe to retain the heat long enough for the wiping operation, drop the ladle and pick up a small cloth known

Fig. 15. Wiping a vertical joint.

as the auxiliary cloth. This is held in the right hand and the wiping cloth in the left hand. The metal is brought to the top of the joint by a movement of both hands, as shown in Fig. 14. Hold the main cloth under the joint, and with the auxiliary cloth, wipe off the surplus solder from each end and roughly mold what is left on top to the shape of the joint, throwing all the hot solder into the wiping cloth. Stock this surplus solder to the bottom of the joint and roughly mold it to the proper shape. Drop the auxiliary cloth and finish the joint to shape with the main cloth, using both hands.

WIPING A BRANCH JOINT

Usually more skill is required in preparing and wiping a branch joint than a regular joint. The operations of preparing the joint for wiping are:

1. Boring.
2. Expanding.
3. Flaring out.
4. Removing burrs.
5. Soiling.
6. Shaving.
7. Setting.

First, the pipe from which a branch is to run is tapped with a tap borer, as in Fig. 16. In using a tap borer, do not insert it far enough for its point to come into contact with the opposite side

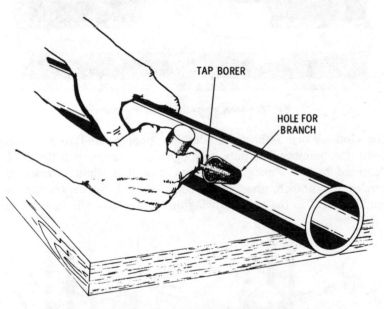

TAP BORER

HOLE FOR BRANCH

Fig. 16. Cutting a branch hole in a lead pipe with a tap borer.

of the pipe. For 1/2- to 1-inch pipe, bore a 5/8-inch hole. The operations that follow consist of removing burrs, soiling, marking off, shaving, and setting, which are performed in a way similar to those for plain or running joints.

In setting, the parts should be secured firmly in position with clamps, blocks, etc. It will be found easier to wipe the joint by setting up the branch in the vertical position. In wiping, pour on the far and near sides, as shown in Fig. 18, holding the cloth at an angle which will distribute the solder over the area to be covered. As the solder begins to flow, it is kept working up by manipulating

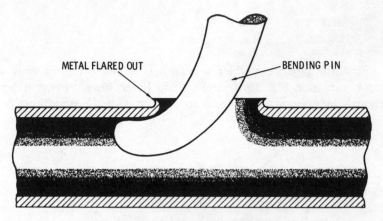

METAL FLARED OUT   BENDING PIN

Fig. 17. Flaring a branch hole in lead pipe.

the cloth. When sufficient solder has been poured to form the joint, the plumber first puts its roughly into shape with the cloth, followed by the wiping movements. The first wiping stroke encircles the branch, the solder being shaped by depressing the middle finger as the cloth is being brought around the ends of the

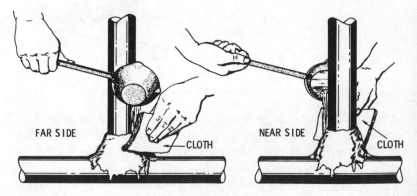

FAR SIDE   CLOTH   NEAR SIDE   CLOTH

Fig. 18. Pouring and wiping vertical branches.

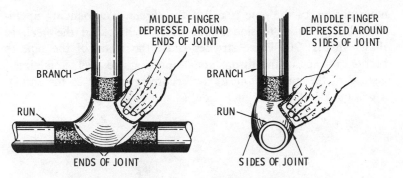

Fig. 19. Movements in wiping vertical branches.

joint, gradually raising this finger as it comes on the sides parallel to the run. These operations are shown in Fig. 19. The stroke should begin on the near side, as far around as possible, so the operator can entirely encircle the branch with one stroke.

BENDING LEAD PIPE

The bending of lead pipe, especially pipes of large diameter, requires skill and a knowledge of the changes which take place in a metal during the bending process. When a pipe is bent, the metal is subjected to stresses which produce compression along the inner wall, or that part of the pipe nearest the center of the curve. This

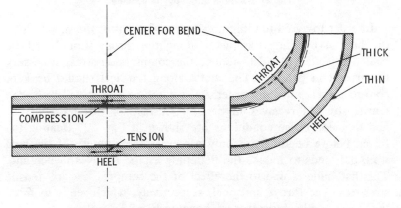

Fig. 20. Length of lead pipe before and after bending.

229

inner portion of the pipe is called the *throat*. The bending operation also produces tension in the outer wall, called the *heel,* as shown in Fig. 20. These stresses cause the metal of the pipe to become thicker at the throat and thinner at the heel. Sometimes, instead of the metal *piling up* or becoming thicker at the throat, it will buckle along the inner side, as shown in Fig. 21.

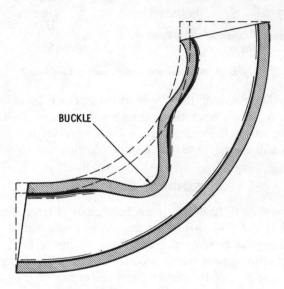

BUCKLE

Fig. 21. Buckle in throat due to bending.

In order to avoid the thinning or drawing out of the metal along the heel in bending, the metal along the throat should first be heated to soften it and to reduce the compression stress necessary to upset it in bending. The metal along the heel should be kept cold to preserve maximum tensile strength so that it will resist the tensile stress it receives in bending, instead of being drawn out and thinned. These conditions are shown in Fig. 22. Heating the throat before bending not only preserves the strength of the heel wall, but tends to reduce the flattening a pipe receives in bending. This flattening is due to the effect of the compression and tensile stresses in the throat and heel, respectively, which tends to force the throat and heel together as shown in Fig. 23.

230

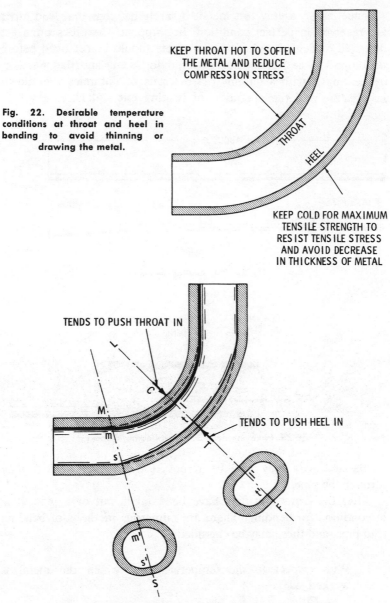

Fig. 22. Desirable temperature conditions at throat and heel in bending to avoid thinning or drawing the metal.

KEEP THROAT HOT TO SOFTEN THE METAL AND REDUCE COMPRESSION STRESS

THROAT

HEEL

KEEP COLD FOR MAXIMUM TENSILE STRENGTH TO RESIST TENSILE STRESS AND AVOID DECREASE IN THICKNESS OF METAL

TENDS TO PUSH THROAT IN

TENDS TO PUSH HEEL IN

Fig. 23. Diagram illustrating the bending force along the throat and heel.

231

Since lead is a very soft metal, it rarely happens that lead pipes are received in perfect condition. In shipping, the pipes often get flattened or dented and all these defects should be removed before bending. The easiest method of removing dents and flat places is by beating it with a dummy. Two forms of dummies are shown in Fig. 24, and the operation of beating out a dent, in Fig. 25.

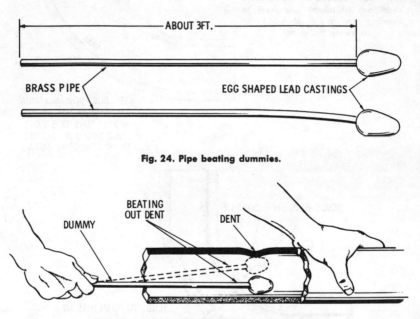

Fig. 24. Pipe beating dummies.

Fig. 25. Removing dents by using beating dummies.

Dents and flats may also be removed by driving a drift plug through the pipe.

After the dents and flats have been taken out of a pipe, it is in condition for bending. There are numerous methods of bending lead pipe, and these may be classified:

1. With respect to the temperature at which the metal is worked, as:
    a. Cold.
    b. Hot.

232

2. With respect to the mode of preventing deformations, as by internal wall support using:
    a. Sand.
    b. Springs.

3. With respect to the mode of correcting deformations, as by:
    a. Internal forces using bobbins or bobbins and followers.
    b. Internal and external dressing.
    c. Cutting and beating.

Bending Cold and Hot

If a small pipe is to be bent cold, the sides parallel to the plane of the bend should be slightly flattened, which will tend to prevent flattening during the bending process. While being bent the pipe will return to its circular cross-sectional form. When small pipes are bent cold, they usually become thicker in the throat and thinner in the heel and, although the circular form is retained on the outside surface in bending cold in a machine, the inside walls will be distended because of the uneven thickness of the metal. The thinning of the metal in the heel (and resulting weakening of the pipe) may be avoided by heating the throat before bending, as has already been explained.

Bending with Internal Wall Supports

To prevent the flattening of lead pipe in bending, sometimes the internal surface of the pipe is held to its original shape by internal supports of incompressible material, such as:

1. Sand.
2. Spring.
3. Rubber rod.

In the first instance, a quantity of sand (sufficient to fill the pipe) is dried by heating, so that it will pack to a firm mass. One end of the pipe is closed with a sand plug and the heated sand then poured in, as shown in Fig. 26. During this operation, the pipe is kept in motion to shake down the sand. When the pipe is apparently full of sand, it should be tapped, which will cause the

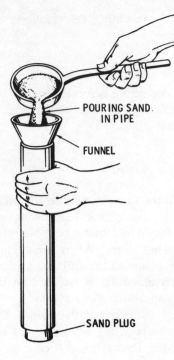

POURING SAND.
IN PIPE

FUNNEL

Fig. 26. Filling pipe with hot sand to
prevent the walls from flattening.

SAND PLUG

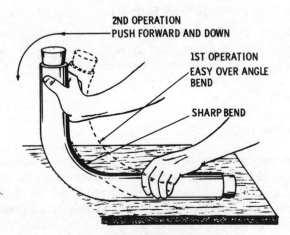

2ND OPERATION
PUSH FORWARD AND DOWN

1ST OPERATION
EASY OVER ANGLE
BEND

SHARP BEND

Fig. 27. Making a bend in the pipe filled with sand.

sand to settle down so that a little more sand can be added. The end should then be closed by inserting a sand plug. The pipe is now bent by manipulating it as shown in Fig. 27, the firmly packed sand inside the pipe holding out the walls in shape.

If a sharp bend is desired, carry an easy bend around past the angle desired, then sharpen up the angle by bending back on the heel, as shown in Fig. 27. An expert plumber can usually make a good bend by bending over the knee, as shown in Fig. 28, but this method is not always good as the pressure on the pipe is not well distributed, resulting in greater distortion of the metal. After the pipe has been bent to shape, any uneven parts should be cor-

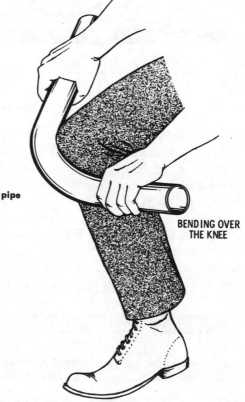

Fig. 28. Method of bending pipe across the knee.

BENDING OVER
THE KNEE

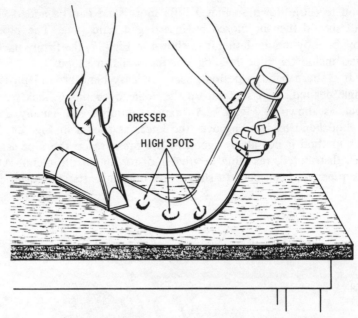

Fig. 29. Dressing down high spots in the bent pipe.

rected by dressing with the dresser, as in Fig. 29. The sand method of bending is desirable for pipes up to 2 inches. Bends in larger sizes are made better by the method of internal forcers, or by internal and external dressing. This method retains the original thickness of the pipe.

Instead of sand support, a spring may be used. The type of spring suitable is shown in Fig. 30, and its application in Fig. 31. In inserting the spring, turn it in the direction in which it is wound, as this reduces the diameter of the convolutions making it easier to insert. If the spring is too snug, it should be rubbed with

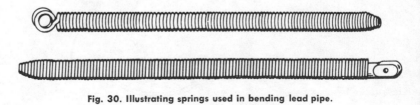

Fig. 30. Illustrating springs used in bending lead pipe.

236

tallow before inserting. Since spring bending is used for small-size pipes (1 to 2 inches in diameter) in which the walls are thicker in proportion than in the larger sizes, there is more distortion (thinning and thickening of the metal in the heel and throat, respectively). To counteract this, it is desirable to heat the pipe along one side previous to bending, the pipe being bent so that the

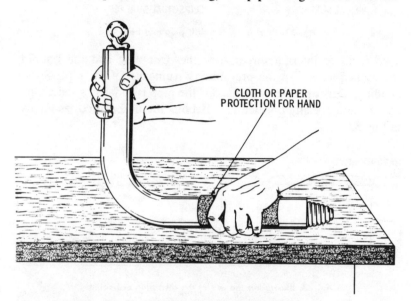

CLOTH OR PAPER
PROTECTION FOR HAND

Fig. 31. Method used in bending lead pipe.

heated part will form the throat. In heating, care should be taken not to overheat, otherwise the temper of the spring will be destroyed or the pipe damaged. The pipe is bent in the usual way, moving the hand along the bend during the operation, but since the pipe has been heated, a cloth or wad of paper will be necessary to protect hand from the heat.

Bending with Internal Forcers

The term *internal forcers* is used here to indicate devices which are placed inside the pipe and which snugly fit the interior walls. When pushed or pulled through the pipe, any dent or flat spot of the wall is forced back to its correct position by a wedge-like action.

237

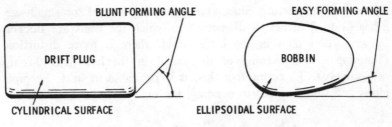

Fig. 32. Illustrating the drift plug and bobbin.

Two types of internal forcers are the drift plug and the bobbin, shown in Fig. 32. In the preliminary truing up of the pipe before bending, a drift plug may be used if the pipe is in fairly good shape, but if there are any big dents, a bobbin should be used, as shown in Fig. 33.

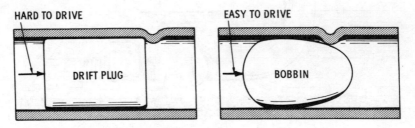

Fig. 33. Illustrating the use of the drift plug or bobbin.

If the pipe is straight and free from dents, make a very slight bend by hand. The small indentation in the throat due to this first bend may be removed by driving through a bobbin with a drive stick, as shown in Fig. 34. The pipe is now bent a few more degrees, and since the curve is too great to permit driving the bobbin with a stick, the bobbin is attached to a small rope and pulled through the pipe by fastening the other end of the rope to some stationary object and pulling the pipe. These operations are repeated for as many successive bendings as are necessary to bring the pipe to the desired curve.

In case of a deep dent or buckle, the aid of a dummy (Fig. 35) preparatory to passing through the bobbin will help. Another method of removing a deep dent or buckle is to pass through a series of graduated bobbins, either by driving or by threading them on a rope and pulling them through. In pulling, a series of sharp jerky pulls should be made, holding the pipe so as to support the bend at the throat. At various stages, the dresser is useful in smoothing out small irregularities.

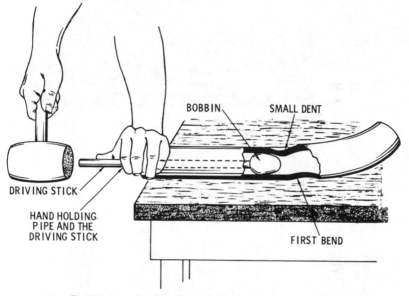

BOBBIN SMALL DENT

DRIVING STICK

HAND HOLDING
PIPE AND THE
DRIVING STICK

FIRST BEND

Fig. 34. Removing the throat distortion by using a bobbin.

A method sometimes employed in making a compound bend, such as an "S" bend, is by using *followers* for driving the bobbin, as shown in Fig. 36. If the followers are too long, they will get jammed in a short bend, and if too short, they will turn or angle. Sometimes a bobbin will split. The bobbin method of bending is well adapted to pipes from 2 to 3 inches in diameter.

Bending by Internal and External Dressing

For pipes larger than 3 inches, bends are made with a dummy since there is sufficient internal space for a stroke long enough to give effective blows. Before beginning to bend the pipe, any dents and flat places are removed with the dummy. The pipe is now heated along the side that is to be the throat of the bend, and the pipe is bent a few degrees at a time. This will cause more or less of a dent in the throat and bulges midway between the throat and heel.

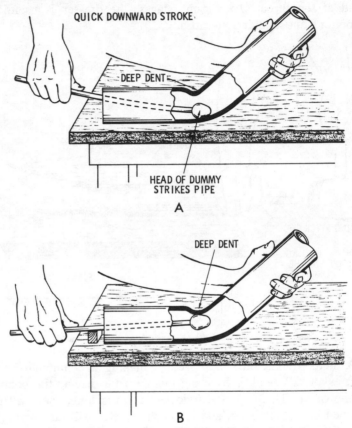

QUICK DOWNWARD STROKE

DEEP DENT

HEAD OF DUMMY
STRIKES PIPE

A

DEEP DENT

B

Fig. 35. Removing the throat and heel distortion by using a dummy.

The dent is removed by using the dummy. The bulges midway between the throat and heel are beaten back to shape with the dresser. These bulges are dressed, not inward, but toward the heel in order to maintain the correct thickness of the metal. An expert will give the dresser an oblique motion which tends to equalize the thickness of the metal building up at the heel and thinning at the throat. The sharpness of the bend is increased by successive bend-

240

ings until the desired curve is obtained, using the dummy and dresser after each bending to remove the distortions. When the pipe has received several bendings, the distortion at the throat cannot be reached by a straight dummy owing to the sharpness of

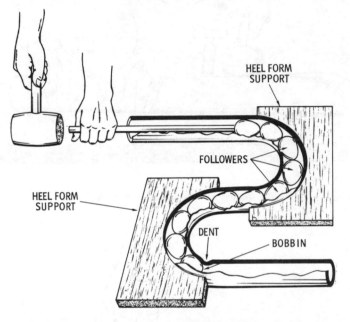

Fig. 36. Using followers to drive the bobbin through a series of curves.

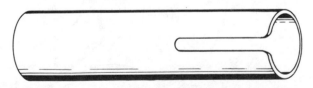

Fig. 37. Cutting a V-notch in pipe to obtain a sharp bend.

the curve. At this stage, the handle of the dummy is curved to conform with the curve of the pipe and used by the *fulcrum method*, as shown in Fig. 35. For the final dressing, a piece of sheet lead about 3 × 10 inches is used as a dresser; it is roughly bent to form a handle by which it is held.

241

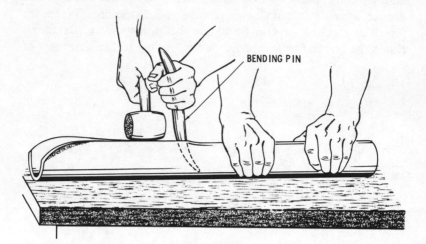

BENDING PIN

Fig. 38. Using a bending pin to cut V-notch in pipe.

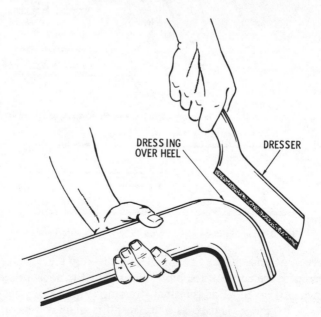

DRESSING
OVER HEEL

DRESSER

Fig. 39. Dressing over the heel which is closed by either
wiping or soldering.

Bending by Cutting and Beating

When a very sharp bend is required (sometimes called a short heel bend), it is best done by cutting away some of the metal to avoid too much distortion. First, tap a small hole in the pipe with the tap borer, and cut a V-notch down to the hole so that the part cut out will have the shape (and proportions to size of pipe) shown in Fig. 37. Run up the end of the V with a bending pin, as shown in Fig. 38, and then dress over the heel as shown in Fig. 39. The seam is closed either by wiping or by soldering.

SUMMARY

Although lead work to the extent of joint wiping is not performed in modern plumbing, it is important for repairs on existing lead pipes in old plumbing systems. Joint-wiping skill is not used extensively by present-day plumbers because of the replacement of lead pipe by copper tubing.

The quality of solder used in lead work is very important, and the plumber must know by its appearance when it contains the right proportions of lead and tin. To preserve the correct proportions of lead and tin, it is necessary to keep the solder from overheating. Overheating solder will burn some of the tin and destroy the correct proportions.

Remove all grease or oil from the pipe by rubbing the surface with sandpaper or a wire brush. The use of soil, which is composed of lamp black and glue, will prevent the solder from spreading to other surfaces of the pipe, thus giving a neat appearance.

REVIEW QUESTIONS

1. What procedures are used to keep the pipe walls from collapsing when bending?

2. What is the purpose of pipe soil?

3. What is a pipe dummy?

4. What is a bobbin?

5. What is a shave hook?

CHAPTER 9

Questions and Answers
For Plumbers

Ques: What is meant by *plumbing*?

Ans: It is the art of installing the pipes, fixtures, and other apparatus in buildings for bringing in the water supply and removing liquid and water-carried wastes.

Ques: What constitutes the plumbing system of a building?

Ans: It includes the water supply distributing pipes, the fixtures and fixture traps, the soil, waste, and vent pipes, the house drain and house sewer, the storm-water drainage, all with their devices, appurtenances, and connections within and adjacent to the building.

Ques: What is a water service pipe?

Ans: It is the pipe from the water main to the building served.

Ques: What is meant by water distribution pipes?

Ans: They are the pipes which convey water from the service pipes to the plumbing fixtures.

Ques: What constitutes the plumbing fixtures?

Ans: These are receptacles intended to receive and discharge water, liquid, or water-carried wastes into a drainage system.

Ques: Why must all plumbing fixtures be connected to a water source?

Ans: In order that they shall be provided with a sufficient amount of water to keep them in a serviceable and sanitary condition.

Ques: What is a trap?

Ans: This is a fitting or device so constructed as to prevent the passage of air or gas through a pipe without materially affecting the flow of sewage or waste water through it.

Ques: What is meant by the vent pipes?

Ans: Any pipe provided to ventilate a house drainage system and to prevent trap siphonage and back pressure.

Ques: What is a local ventilating pipe?

Ans: A pipe through which foul air is removed from a room or a fixture.

Ques: What is a soil pipe?

Ans: Any pipe which conveys the discharge of water closets, with or without the discharges from other fixtures, to the house drain.

Ques: What is a waste pipe?

Ans: A pipe which receives the discharge of any fixture except water closets, and conveys the same to the house drain, soil, or waste stacks.

Ques: What constitutes a main?

Ans: The main of any system of horizontal, vertical, or continuous piping, is that part of the system which receives the wastes and vents or back vents from fixture outlets or traps direct or through branch pipes.

Ques: What is meant by branch piping?

Ans: That part of the system which extends horizontally at a slight grade, with or without lateral or vertical extensions or vertical arms, from the main to receive fixture outlets not directly connected to the main.

Ques: What is a stack?

Ans: Stack is a general term for any vertical line of soil, waste, or vent piping.

Ques: What is meant by the term *house drain?*

Ans: It is that part of the lowest horizontal piping of a house drainage system which receives the discharge from soil, waste, and other drainage pipes inside the walls of any building, and conveys the same to the house sewer beginning 5 feet outside of the inner face of the building wall.

Ques: What is a house sewer?

Ans: It is that part of the horizontal piping of a house drainage system extending from the house drain 5 feet outside of the inner face of the building wall to its connection with the main sewer or cesspool, and conveying the drainage from one building site.

Ques: What is meant by the term *pipe size* and *pipe length*?

Ans: The given caliber of size of pipes is for a normal internal diameter. Copper and brass pipe sizes are measured by their outside diameter. The length of a pipe means the developed length; the length along the center line of pipe and fittings.

Ques: What is a dead end?

Ans: A branch leading from a soil, waste, vent, house drain, or house sewer, which is terminated at a developed distance of 2 feet or more by means of a cap, plug, or other fitting not used for admitting water to the pipe.

Ques: What are the rules as to workmanship and materials?

Ans: All work must be performed in a thorough, workmanlike manner, and all material used in any drainage or plumbing system or part thereof shall be free from defects.

Ques: How is it possible to determine if the pipes used are of the proper size and weight?

Ans: The length of each pipe, fitting, trap, fixture, and device used in a plumbing or drainage system shall be stamped or indelibly marked with the weight or quality, and the marker's mark or name.

Ques: What is the maximum length of *short branches* of 1-1/2 inch lead pipe?

Ans: 5 feet.

Ques: What kind of material is employed for outside leaders, and how should they be connected to the drainage system?

Ans: Outside leaders shall be made of sheet metal, copper, or plastic, and shall be connected with the house drain system by

247

means of a cast-iron pipe extending vertically 5 feet above the grade level.

Ques: When may the house sewer be of earthenware pipe?

Ans: Only when a proper foundation can be obtained consisting of a natural bed of earth, rock, etc.

Ques: What kind of material must be employed in all main, soil, waste, or vent pipes?

Ans: All main, soil, waste, and vent pipes must be made of iron, steel, or brass. (Some local codes allow plastic pipes).

Ques: What is meant by the term *riser lines* in a plumbing system?

Ans: The term *riser* is generally applied to the vertical lines extending through the building from its connection with the house main.

Ques: May cast-iron pipe be used in a plumbing system?

Ans: If the cast-iron pipe conforms to the standard specifications of the American Society for Testing Materials. All cast-iron pipe and fittings for underground use shall be coated with asphaltum or coal-tar pitch.

Ques: What are the requirements when brass and copper pipe is used?

Ans: All brass and copper pipe shall conform to the standard specification of the A.S.T.M.

Ques: What are the rules when making connection between iron and brass pipes?

Ans: Such connections must never be made with slip joints, and the threaded connection on the iron pipe must be of the same size as that on the brass pipe, and all burrs or cuttings shall be removed.

Ques: What are the requirements when making joints in vitrified pipes?

Ans: All joints in vitrified clay pipes, or between vitrified clay pipes and metals, shall be poured joints.

Ques: How should a calked joint be made?

Ans: All calked joints shall be firmly packed with oakum or hemp, and shall be secured only with pure lead not less than 1 inch deep, well calked. No paint, varnish, or putty will be permitted until the joint is tested.

Ques: How is an approved joint in lead pipe or between lead and brass or copper pipe made?

Ans: Joints in lead pipe, or between lead pipe and brass or copper pipe, ferrules, soldering nipples, bushings or traps, in all cases on the sewer side of the trap, and in concealed joints on the inlet side of the trap, shall be full-wiped joints with an exposed surface of the solder to each side of the joint of not less than 3/4 inch, and a minimum thickness at the thickest part of the joint of not less than 3/8 inch.

Ques: What are the requirements when joints are made between lead and cast or wrought iron?

Ans: The joints shall be made by means of a calking ferrule, soldering nipple, or bushing.

Ques: When may slip joints and unions be used?

Ans: Slip joints will be permitted only in trap seals or on the inlet side of the trap. Unions on the sewer side of the trap shall be ground faced, and shall not be concealed or enclosed.

Ques: What is the term used for a fitting that makes an angle between two adjacent pipes?

Ans: Elbow.

Ques: What is the name used for a fitting that has one side outlet at right angles to the run?

Ans: Tee.

Ques: What is the name employed for a fitting having a larger size at one end than on the other?

Ans: Reducer.

Ques: What is the name of a fitting which has one side outlet at any angle other than 90°

Ans: Wye.

Ques: What is the term generally employed for a piece of pipe which is threaded on both ends and less than 12 inches long?
Ans: Nipple.

Ques: What is the minimum diameter of brass pipe used in riser lines of a plumbing system?
Ans: One-half inch.

Ques: What should be the minimum distance between the hot- and cold-water risers in a plumbing system?
Ans: The distance between the hot- and cold-water risers where a hot-water supply is installed should not be less than 6 inches, and where conditions encountered are such that they cannot be readily placed 6 inches or more apart, the hot-water riser should be covered with an approved insulating material so as not to interfere with the prompt delivery of hot water to the faucet when required.

Ques: What is the minimum size of a main vent pipe?
Ans: The size of a main vent pipe must never be less than 2 inches in diameter.

Ques: How are the required sizes of vent pipes determined?
Ans: The size of main vents or vent stacks shall be determined from the size of the soil or waste stack vented and the total number of units drained into it. However, they must not be less than the following: for water closets on three or more floors, 3 inches in diameter; for other fixtures where the building is less than 7 floors in height, 2 inches in diameter; where the building is less than 9 stories in height, 3 inches in diameter; from 8 to 16 stories and less in height, 4 inches in diameter, etc. For all fixtures other than water closets and slop sinks, and for buildings more than 8 stories in height, the vent pipes may be 1 inch smaller in diameter than above stated.

Ques: What are the requirements in regard to the sizes of long branch vent pipes?
Ans: No branch vent pipe shall be less than 1-1/2 inches in diameter, and for long branch vent pipes over 10 feet, but not exceeding 25 feet in length, 2 inches in diameter; when over 25 feet, but not more than 50 feet in length, 3 inches in diameter.

Ques: What is the longest branch vent pipes permitted?
Ans: No branch vent pipe must exceed 50 feet in length.

Ques: Where shall a clean-out be placed in a vertical waste or soil stack?
Ans: A clean-out easily accessible shall be provided and placed at the foot of each vertical waste or soil stack.

Ques: How may waste or soil pipes be protected against obstruction?
Ans: By the use of strong metallic strainers placed over the outlets.

Ques: Should each building have soil and waste stacks?
Ans: Yes. Every building in which plumbing fixtures are installed shall have a soil and waste stack extending full size through the roof.

Ques: How far above the roof must soil or vent pipe lines be carried?
Ans: All roof extensions of soil and vent stacks shall be run full size at least 1 foot above the roof coping, and when the roof is used for other purposes than weather protection, such extension shall not be less than 5 feet above the roof.

Ques: What special rules apply to soil and vent pipes used in a cold climate?
Ans: Where there is danger of frost closure, no roof extension shall be less than 4 inches in diameter. The change in diameter must be accomplished by the use of a long increase at least 1 foot below the roof, and where the access to the roof is difficult, a test opening shall be provided at this point.

Ques: May a vent or soil pipe be terminated within a distance of 2 feet from any door, window, scuttle, or air shaft?
Ans: No. The roof terminal of any stack or vent, if within 12 feet of any door, window, scuttle, or air shaft, shall extend at least 3 feet above the same.

Ques: May soil or vent lines be carried outside of buildings?
Ans: No soil or vent lines shall be installed or permitted out-

side of a building unless adequate provision is made to protect it from frost.

Ques: Where shall main vents be connected?

Ans: All main vents or vent stacks shall connect full size at their base to the main soil or vent pipe at or below the lowest fixture branch, and shall extend undiminished in size above the roof, and shall be reconnected with the main soil or waste vent at least 3 feet above the highest fixture branch.

Ques: When offsets are made in vent lines, how shall they be connected?

Ans: All vent and branch vent lines shall be connected and installed in such a way that they are free from drops or sags, and be so graded and connected as to drip back to the soil or waste pipe by gravity. Where the vent pipes connect to a horizontal soil or waste pipe, the vent branch shall be taken off above the center line of the pipe, and the vent pipes must rise vertically, or at an angle of 45°, to a point 6 inches above the fixture it is venting before offsetting horizontally or connecting to the branch, main waste, or soil vent.

Ques: When may circuit or loop vents be employed?

Ans: A circuit or loop vent will be permitted as follows: A branch soil or waste pipe to which two and not more than eight water closets, pedestal urinals, trap standard slop sinks, or shower stalls are connected in series, may be vented by a circuit or loop vent, which shall be taken off in front of the last fixture connection. Where fixtures discharge above such branches, each branch shall be provided with a relief one-half the diameter of the soil or waste stack, taken off in front of the first fixture connection.

Ques: What is the required running diameter of traps for urinals?

Ans: 2 inches in diameter.

Ques: What are the requirements for a permissible trap?

Ans: Every trap shall be self-cleaning. All traps used for bath tubs, lavatories, sinks, and other similar fixtures shall be of lead, brass, cast iron, galvanized malleable iron, or porcelain enameled inside. Galvanized or porcelain enameled traps shall be extra heavy and shall have a full-bore smooth-interior waterway, with threads tapped out of solid metal. Some local codes allow the use of plastic materials and traps.

Ques: Where shall the fixture trap be placed relative to its fixture?

Ans: The trap shall be placed as close to the fixture as possible, but shall in no case be placed more than 24 inches away from the fixture.

Ques: What are the requirements in regard to clean-outs in fixture traps?

Ans: All traps, except water-closet traps, shall be provided with an accessible brass trap screw of ample size, protected by the water seal.

Ques: May fixture traps be connected in series?

Ans: No. The discharge from any fixture shall never pass through more than one trap on its way to the house drain.

Ques: Must all fixture traps be protected against back pressure and siphonage?

Ans: Yes. Every fixture trap shall be protected against siphonage and back pressure, and air circulation assured by means of a soil or waste stack vent, a continuous waste or soil vent, or a loop or circuit vent. No crown vent shall be installed.

Ques: Must trap levels be protected against frost and evaporation?

Ans: All traps shall be installed true with respect to their water seals and protected from frost and evaporation.

Ques: What is the seal of a trap?

Ans: It is the depth of the water between the dip and the outlet of the trap. The effectiveness of a trap always depends on its water seal.

Ques: What is the dip of a trap?

Ans: The dip is that part of a trap that dips into the seal, and under which all waste matter must pass.

253

Ques: What are the terms used for some of the common styles of traps?

Ans: "S" trap; 3/4 "S" trap; 1/2 "S" trap; grease trap; sand trap, etc.

Ques: What is meant by the term *siphonage?*

Ans: By referring to an "S" trap, it will be readily seen that the outlet forms a most perfect siphon; the part of the trap between the dip and the outlet forming the short side, and the waste pipe from the outlet downward forming the long side. When a large quantity of water is discharged from the fixture into the trap, the water fills the entire trap and waste pipe for some distance below the trap. It is readily observed that the weight of the water is much greater at the outlet side than at the inlet side of the trap, and it tends to cause the water in the trap to rise to the outlet and follow the larger body of water in the waste pipe, leaving the trap without any water to form its water seal.

Ques: What determines the resistance against siphonage in a trap?

Ans: It is the depth of the water seal that determines the amount of resistance a trap will offer to being unsealed by siphonage.

Ques: How should service pipes be protected when exposed to frost?

Ans: They should be protected by a sufficient amount of felt or other insulation, spun glass, etc., and supported by metal sleeves or approved metal bands.

Ques: What precautions should be taken when thawing a frozen water pipe?

Ans: If the thawing is accomplished by means of a blow torch or hot water, the thawing medium should be applied to the water-supply end of the pipe, opening a faucet if possible to indicate when the flow of water starts. It is well to keep in mind that the middle of the pipe should never be thawed first, because expansion of the water confined by ice on both sides may burst the pipe.

Ques: How should a waste or sewer pipe be thawed out?

Ans: When thawing a waste or sewer pipe, always work upward from the lower end, to permit the water to drain away.

Ques: Enumerate and briefly discuss the most effective methods used to thaw out frozen water pipes.

Ans: The method to be used will be determined by the amount of pipe to be thawed, as well as the size and location. For short lengths of exposed pipe, boiling hot water or hot cloths have proven to be effective. If there is no danger of fire, or if the necessary precautions against fire are observed, a blow torch or burning newspaper run back and forth along the frozen water pipe gives quick results. When the pipe to be thawed is located underground, or is otherwise inaccessible, the pipe should be disconnected at the house end and boiling water directed through the opening by means of a small piece of auxiliary pipe or rubber tubing to which a funnel conveniently is attached. Chemicals are more often resorted to as a preventive against frost than for thawing pipes already frozen, and should if possible be avoided as a thawing medium because of their often dangerous characteristics. When a long section of inaccessible piping or leaders are to be thawed, low-voltage electricity has been found to be effective, particularly with electric heating cables. Electric blankets have been used with success.

Ques: What is the amount of water required for a water closet or pedestal urinal for one flushing?

Ans: All water closets or pedestal urinals shall be flushed by means of an approved tank or flush valve, having a flushing capacity of at least 4 gallons for water closets, and at least 2 gallons for urinals, and shall be properly adjusted so as to prevent the waste of water.

Ques: What is the minimum diameter required for the flush pipe in a water-closet flush tank?

Ans: The flush pipe for water-closet flush tanks shall not be less than 1-1/4 inches in diameter.

Ques: How many water closets are required on a floor of a lodging house in which 24 persons reside?

Ans: Two. According to the plumbing code, there must be a sufficient number of water closets on each floor, and so that, in any case, there never will be more than 15 persons to each water closet.

Ques: How shall the water supply to a building be controlled?

Ans: A main shut-off on the water supply line shall be provided near the curb. Accessible shut-offs shall also be provided on the main supply line just inside the foundation wall for each flat or apartment of a building, for each lawn sprinkler, for the supply to each hot-water tank, and for each water closet.

Ques: Must water supply pipes and storage tanks be protected against frost?

Ans: Yes. All concealed water pipes and storage tanks and all exposed pipes or storage tanks subject to freezing temperatures shall be efficiently protected against freezing.

Ques: What material should water supply pipes and fittings consist of?

Ans: All water supply pipes for a plumbing system shall be of lead, galvanized wrought iron or steel, brass, copper, or cast iron, with brass or galvanized cast-iron or galvanized malleable-iron fittings. Pipe or fittings that have been used for another purpose shall not be used for distribution of water. Some local codes allow plastic pipe to be used.

Ques: What size of pipes is required in a water supply system?

Ans: All water supply pipes of any building shall be of a size sufficient to permit a continuous ample flow of water on all floors at any given time.

Ques: May the over-flow pipe from a house water supply tank be connected to the house drain?

Ans: No. All pipes from water supply tanks shall **not be directly** connected with any house drain, soil, or waste pipe, but shall discharge upon the roof or be trapped into an open fixture.

Ques: May the refrigerator waste pipe be connected to the house drain?

Ans: No. The waste pipe from a refrigerator or ice box, or any other receptacle where food is stored, shall not be connected with any house drain, soil, or waste pipe.

Ques: How then shall refrigerator waste pipes be connected?
Ans: Refrigerator, ice-box, or food-container waste pipes shall empty into an open sink that is properly supplied with water and is connected, trapped, and vented the same as any other fixtures, or they may discharge into a downspout or rain-leader trap located inside the building, or into a cellar floor drain, but their ends must be left open.

Ques: What precautions should be observed when installing waste pipe lines for a refrigeration system?
Ans: Refrigerator waste pipes shall not be less than 1-1/4 inches for one opening, 1-1/2 inches for three openings, and 2 inches for four to twelve openings. Each opening shall have a trap and a clean-out at an angle so arranged as to properly clean and flush the pipe. Such waste pipes shall be continued at not less than full size through the roof, except where such fixtures are located in the basement or first floor.

Ques: Where may cesspools be constructed?
Ans: Cesspools may be constructed only in nonresidential areas where no sewer exists, and only if no health hazard will result from the installation and its use.

Ques: Where should cesspools be located relative to building?
Ans: The distance between cesspool and any building on the same lot as the building for which the use is intended shall be as follows:

From any source of domestic water supply

	Recommended	100 feet
From any structure	Recommended	20 feet
From any lot line	Recommended	10 feet
From any septic tank	Recommended	10 feet

From other seepage pits at least three times
the diameter of the larger pit.

257

Ques: How should a cesspool be constructed?

Ans: A cesspool of average proportion should be 6 to 9 feet in diameter, lined with brick laid without mortar, and from 7 to 12 feet in depth. The brick lining should be 8 inches thick, and the bottom of stone or concrete 6 inches thick. Sometimes the top is arched and capped on the ground surface by a cover of wood, stone, or cast iron. When the walls are carried straight up, the top should be covered with impregnated boards or planks of substantial dimensions, and the entire structure may be conveniently hidden with a hedge or shrubbery.

Ques: How often should cesspools be cleaned and emptied?

Ans: Cesspools should be cleaned and emptied at least once a year and the contents given a safe burial, with the requisite permission vested in some municipal sewage system authorities. After cleaning, the walls and bottom should be treated with a disinfectant or a deodorant.

Ques: When should cesspools be made of watertight construction, as shown in Fig. 1?

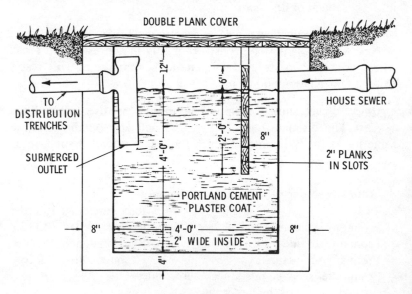

Fig. 1. A one-chamber cesspool tank.

Ans: Only in instances where facilities for removal and disposal of the contents in a clean and effective manner are available.

Ques: What is the difference between a septic tank and a cesspool?

Ans: A septic tank is a well-regulated and controlled cesspool. Cesspools should be considered only as a temporary expedient until connections to a public sewer can be made within a reasonable time.

Ques: How can obstructions in a house sewer be removed?

Ans: By the use of some of the simple tools shown in Fig. 2. Some of these tools can be readily made at home or by a blacksmith, and most of them should be obtainable for temporary use from hardware stores, lumber dealers, or other local business firms that loan tools for a small fee. Power rodding equipment is also available from rental sources.

Ques: What are the causes of sewer obstruction, and how should sewers be constructed to lessen this trouble?

Ans: Causes of sewer obstruction may be any one of the following: Broken pipes, insufficient grade to give cleansing velocities, newspaper, rags, garbage or other solids in the sewage, congealing of grease in pipes and house sewer traps, and poor joint construction whereby rootlets grow into the sewer and choke it. The proper grade and good construction, with particular care given to the joints, will avert or lessen these troubles. The sewer should be made perfectly straight with the interior of the joints scraped or swabbed smooth. When the joint-filling material has set, the hollows beneath the hubs should be filled with good earth free of stones, well tamped or puddled in place. It is important that like material be used at the sides of the pipe and above it for at least one foot. No running traps should be placed in the house sewer because they are liable to become obstructed and prevent free movement of air through the sewer and soil stack. Conductors or drains for rain or other clean water should not be connected to the house sewer, but should discharge into a water course or other outlet.

259

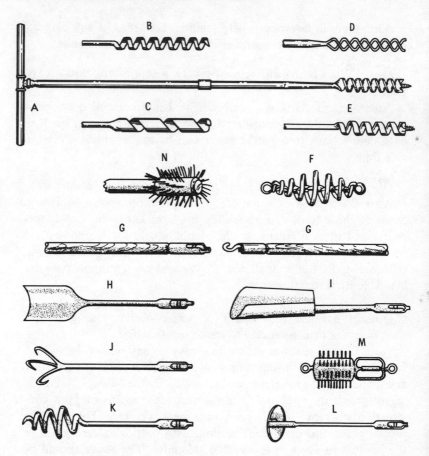

Fig. 2. Several different types of sewer cleaning tools. (A) thru (E) various type augers; (F) root cutter; (G) sewer rod; (H) gouge; (I) scoop; (J) claw; (K) screw; (L) scraper; (M) wire brush.

Ques: What is a siphon chamber and how does it work?

Ans: The purpose of a siphon chamber is to secure intermittent discharge, thus allowing a considerable period of time for one dose to work off in the soil and for air to enter the soil spaces before another flush is received. It is also used to secure distribution over a larger area and in a more even manner than where the sewage is allowed to dribble and produce the conditions of the old-fashioned sink drain, namely, a small area of water-logged ground.

Three types of sewage siphons are shown in Fig. 3. In all, the essential principle is the same. A column of air is entrapped between two columns of water; when the water in the chamber rises to a predetermined height, called the discharge line, the pressure forces out the confined air, upsetting the balance and causing a

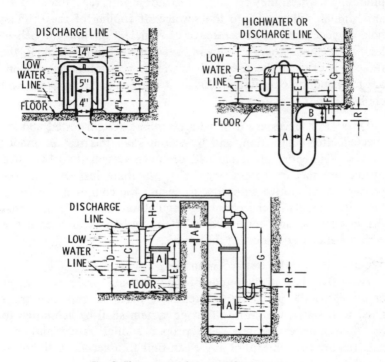

Fig. 3. Three types of sewer siphon systems.

rush of water through to the sewer. The entire operation is fully automatic and very simple. The siphons shown are commercial products and made of cast iron. Their simplicity and reliability are enhanced by the small number of nonmovable parts.

Manufacturers furnish full information for setting the siphons and putting them in operation. For example, for type 2 in Fig. 3: (1) set siphon trap (U-shaped pipe) plumb, making E (height from floor to top of long leg) as specified; (2) fill siphon trap with water till it begins to **run out at B**; (3) **place bell in position of top**

261

of long leg, and the siphon is ready for service. Do not fill vent pipe on side of bell. The overhead siphon (type 3, Fig. 3) may be installed readily in a tank already built by the addition of an outlet pump. If properly set and handled, sewage siphons require very little attention and flush with certainty. However, like all plumbing fixtures, they are subject to stoppage if rags, newspapers, and similar solids get into the sewage. If fouling of the sniffling hole or vent prevents the entrance of sufficient air into the bell to lock the siphon properly, allowing sewage to dribble through, the remedy is to clean the siphon. It is well to remember that siphons are for handling only liquid; sludge, if allowed to accumulate, will choke them.

Ques: Is it necessary to have a plumbing system tested and inspected after completion, and by whom shall this test be made?

Ans: The entire plumbing and drainage system shall be tested by the plumber in the presence of a plumbing inspector, or the proper administrative authority, to ensure the compliance with all the requirements of the plumbing regulations, and to ensure that the installation and construction of the system is in accordance with the approved plans and the permit.

Ques: How is this test accomplished?

Ans: By filling all the piping of the plumbing system with water or air. After the plumbing fixtures have been set and their traps filled with water, the entire drainage system shall be submitted to the final air-pressure test. The proper administrative authority may require the removal of any clean-outs to ascertain if the pressure has reached all parts of the system.

Ques: How shall the water test be made?

Ans: The water test may be applied to the drainage system in its entirety or in sections. If applied to the entire system, all openings in the piping shall be tightly closed, except the highest opening above the roof and the system filled with water to the point of overflow above the roof. If the system is tested in sections, each opening shall be tightly plugged, except the highest opening of the section under test, and each section shall be filled with water; but no section shall be tested with less than a 10 foot head of water or with less than 5 pounds of air pressure. In testing successive sections, at least the upper 10 feet of the next preceding section shall be retested, so that no joint or pipe in the building shall have been submitted to a test of less than a 10-foot head of water or 5 pounds of air pressure.

Ques: How shall the air test be made?

Ans: By attaching the air compressor or test apparatus to any suitable opening, and closing all other air inlets and outlets to the system, then forcing air into the system until there is uniform pressure of 5 pounds per square inch, or sufficient to balance a 10-inch column of mercury.

Ques: How long shall this air pressure be maintained in the drainage system?

Ans: For at least 15 minutes.

Ques: How shall the final air test be made?

Ans: In the final air test, the air machine shall be connected to any suitable opening or outlet, and air pressure equivalent to a 1-inch water column shall be applied and left standing at least 15 minutes. If there is no leakage or forcing of trap seals indicated by the fluctuation of the drum, float, or water column, the system shall be deemed airtight.

Ques: In what order may the tests be made?

Ans: Separately, or as follows: 1. The house sewer and all its branches from the property line to the house drain. 2. The house drain and yard drains, including all piping to the height of 10 feet above the highest point on the house drain, except the exposed connections to fixtures. 3. The soil, waste, vent, inside conductor, and drainage pipe which should be covered up before the building is enclosed or ready for completion. (The test required for 2 and 3 may be combined.) 4. The final test of the whole system. 5. After each of the tests has been made, the proper administrative authority shall issue a written approval.

Ques: What is a relief valve?

Ans: It is a valve arranged to provide an automatic relief in case of excess pressure.

Ques: What is a safety valve?

Ans: It is a relief valve for expansive fluids and is provided with a chamber to control the amount of blow-back before the valve reseats.

Ques: What is a stop valve?

Ans: It is a valve of the globe type used to shut off a line.

Ques: What is a back-pressure valve?

Ans: It is a valve similar to a low-pressure safety valve which is set to maintain a certain back pressure on feed operating pressure irrespective of pressure variations of the supply. The back-pressure valve is arranged to relieve any excess supply to the atmosphere or elsewhere, and it opens and closes automatically as required to produce this result.

Ques: What is meant by the term electrolysis?

Ans: It is generally applied to electrolytic corrosion due to electic current conduction by water, gas mains, or metallic structures.

Ques: Where does electrolysis take place?

Ans: Along water mains or metallic structures, where the electric stray current leaves the metal for the ground or some other conductor of less resistance.

Ques: Where is this electrolytic corrosion most common?

Ans: In densely populated areas along electric railroad lines where track rails are utilized as a negative return circuit.

Ques: How can electrolysis be avoided or lessened?

Ans: By lowering the voltage drop by increasing the metallic area of the negative return circuits adjacent to the water mains. In some cases, insulating or installing high-resistance pipe joints have been found to limit the conduction of stray electrical currents.

Ques: Name other methods of lessening the danger of electrolysis.

Ans: By increasing the resistance of the road-bed, by making it dry, and insulating the ties by creosote or similar preservative.

Ques: How may an electric current be detected in a main?

Ans: By means of a sensitive galvanometer which can be calibrated to show the potential drop along the pipe, measuring the distance, and calculating the cross-sectional area. The potential drop divided by the resistance gives the flow of current in the main. By knowing the direction of the flow, its amount, and the efficiency of corrosion, the actual damage being done by electrolysis may be calculated as a definite weight of metal per annum.

Ques: What are the essential requirements of piping and apparatus for fire protection?

Ans: It must be capable of producing, without question, the desired performance, and it must be designed so as to function invariably, regardless of age or weather conditions.

Ques: Who establishes rules for all kinds of fire protective apparatus?

Ans: The National Board of Fire Underwriters and allied organizations.

Ques: How should the piping for an automatic sprinkler system be designed?

Ans: It must be designed so as to ensure: 1. An adequate and reliable water supply. 2. Ample and complete distribution. 3. Proper protection against freezing.

Ques: What are the rules in regard to water supply?

Ans: It is generally considered necessary to have two sources of water supply, one which should require no manual operation. For example, a common arrangement is a gravity tank in combination with a fire-department connection to be used when the apparatus arrives.

Ques: What are the N.B.F.U. rules in regards to location and spacing of sprinkler heads?

Ans: They take into account the type of building construction and the dimension of the bays. In general, one sprinkler head is required for each 80 to 100 square feet of floor area.

Ques: What is the relation between the number of heads and branch pipes?

Ans: Piping should be so arranged that the number of heads on any branch pipe does not exceed eight.

Ques: What should be the size of riser lines in a sprinkler system?

Ans: Each riser in a sprinkler system should be of sufficient size to supply all the sprinklers connected to it on any one floor, or if there is no approved fire stop between the floors, the riser should be of sufficient size to accommodate the total number of sprinklers.

Ques: Must riser and supply lines be protected against frost?

Ans: If in exposed locations, they must be adequately protected against frost by means of insulating materials.

Ques: What type of valves may be used on a fire-protective system?

Ans: All valves must be of the O.S. & Y. pattern, and check valves should be installed in all sources of supply. Each system should be provided with a gate valve located to control all sources of water supply except that from fire-departmental sources.

Ques: What is a *dry system,* and where is such a system required?

Ans: It is a system in which the piping is ordinarily filled with air at a pressure considerably lower than water pressure. When a sprinkler head opens, water enters the system and drives the air out ahead of it. This type of system is required in rooms which cannot be properly heated.

Ques: What is the most important feature of the dry system?

Ans: It is the dry-pipe valve, a device which normally prevents water from entering the system but which opens when the air pressure is lowered due to the opening of a head.

Ques: What is the water source for an automatic sprinkler system?

Ans: A municipal system under pressure or overhead gravity tanks are used for automatic sprinklers and hose connections.

Ques: What materials are the tanks made of?

Ans: They may be made of either wood staves or steel.

Ques: How are the required tank sizes determined?

Ans: The size of a tank for a given service is determined individually by the insurance authorities. In general, when feeding sprinklers, the tank must have a capacity of 10,000 to 25,000 gallons. When feeding both sprinklers and hose, a minimum capacity of 30,000 gallons is usually required.

Ques: What is the size of discharge pipes relative to tank capacity in an elevated gravity-tank system?

Ans: Elevated gravity tanks must have a discharge pipe of not less than 6 inches for tank sizes up to 25,000 gallons capacity, and generally not less than 8 inches for 30,000 up to 110,000 gallons, and 10 inches for greater capacities.

Ques: How are the tanks protected against freezing?

Ans: The usual arrangement consists of a tubular steam heater to which a connection is made from the base of the tank discharge pipe. The heated water is carried up to the tank by a separate pipe. This arrangement permits the temperature of the coldest water to be observed readily and is by far the simplest and most reliable method. The coldest water should not be allowed to go below 40°F.

Ques: What are the regulations in regard to pressure tanks?

Ans: Pressure tanks for fire service are ordinarily kept two-thirds full of water, and with an air pressure on the surface of the water of 75 pounds plus three times the pressure caused by the column of water in the sprinkler system above the tank bottom.

Ques: What is the capacity of pressure tanks?

Ans: The capacity is usually set by the insurance inspection authorities having jurisdiction, and is usually between 4,500 and 9,000 gallons per tank.

Ques: How should a pressure tank be designed?

Ans: It should be in accordance with the rules for unfired pressure vessels of the A.S.M.E.

Ques: What determines the use of house supply tanks?

Ans: When the water pressure is not sufficient to supply all fixtures freely and continuously, a house supply tank shall be

267

provided. The tank shall be adequate to supply all fixtures at all times.

Ques: What method shall be used to supply house tanks?

Ans: House supply tanks shall be supplied from the street pressure or, when necessary, by power pumps. When such tanks are supplied from the street pressure, ball cocks shall be provided.

Ques: Where shall the water supply inlet to roof tanks be located?

Ans: Water supply inlets to roof tanks shall be located at least 2 inches above the overflow pipe level of the tank, and shall be equipped with an automatic ball stop. The outlet from a roof tank to the distribution system in the building shall be effectively equipped to prevent solids from entering into such piping. All down-feed supplies from a tank, cross connected in any manner with distribution supply piping in a building supplied by direct street main or pump pressure, shall be equipped with a check valve to prevent back flow of water into the roof tank.

Ques: May a gravity tank be directly connected to the city water main?

Ans: No gravity tank shall be directly connected to the city water main, but shall be provided with an over-the-rim filler, the orifice of the outlet of which must be elevated a distance equal to the least diameter of such water discharging orifice or outlet, and in no case less than 1 inch above the top rim of the tank.

Ques: What size discharge pipe shall be provided for a gravity tank having a capacity of 500 gallons or more?

Ans: The discharge pipe from a gravity tank of 500 gallons or more capacity shall be at least 4 inches nominal diameter for a distance of not less than 4 feet, and in no case shall it be smaller than the main section of the riser. The shut-off valve shall be the same size as the outlet from the tank, but not less than a 4-inch gate valve.

Ques: What are the rules for the design of house supply tanks?

Ans: Gravity house supply tanks shall be built of wood or steel, or of wood lined with tinned and planished copper, and such tanks shall be supported on steel beams. Such tanks shall be provided with suitable covers. Pressure tanks shall be cylindrical closed vessels and shall be built of steel, unless otherwise specified. Such tanks shall be designed for at least the working pressure under which they are to operate.

Ques: What are the rules with regards to the overflow pipes for house supply tanks?

Ans: Overflow pipes for gravity tanks shall discharge, whenever possible, above and within 6 inches of the roof. Where such discharge is impossible, such overflow pipes shall be trapped and discharged over an open water-supplied sink 3-1/2 feet or less above the floor, or connected through a check valve to a leader. It shall be unlawful to connect overflow pipes with any part of the plumbing, except as provided above. Overflow pipes shall be at least one commercial size larger than the supply pipe, but where the capacity of tanks is 500 gallons or more, the minimum size of such pipes shall be 4 inches.

Ques: What pipe sizes are required for the emptying pipes on house supply tanks?

Ans: Emptying pipes shall be provided for house supply tanks and discharged as required for overflow pipes. Each tank shall be provided with emptying pipes having the following minimum diameters: a. 2-1/2 inches for a tank of 5000 and more gallons. b. 3 inches for a tank of more than 5000 and less than 10,000 gallons. c. 4 inches for a tank of more than 10,000 gallons. Each emptying pipe shall have a valve of the same diameter as the pipe.

Ques: What are the rules governing ball cocks on house supply tanks?

Ans: Ball cocks controlling the water supply to suction, roof, or intermediate tanks shall be located at least 1 inch above the flood level rim of the tank. In roof tanks equipped with an overflow of a size at least one commercial diameter larger than the water supply pipe, the ball cock may be located 2 inches above the highest elevation of the overflow pipe. The overflow and emptying pipes of a roof, suction, or intermediate tanks shall not be directly connected to a drainage system.

269

Ques: What are the rules governing cleaning and painting of water tanks?

Ans: (1) No water tank of any kind which is part of a building water supply system used for domestic purposes shall be cleaned with any material or painted on the inside in any manner that will affect the taste or potability of the water when the tank is put into service. The water supply connections to and from a tank shall be disconnected or effectually plugged while the tank is being cleaned or painted to prevent any foreign fluid or substance from entering the distribution piping. Where the air in a tank may be inadequate to sustain human life, or may contain an injurious gas, adequate measures shall be taken for the protection of the workman. (2) After the tank has been cleaned or painted it shall be disinfected as follows before it is put back in service: (a) The inner side of the top, bottom, and walls shall be washed with a hypochlorite solution containing 25 parts or more per million of available chlorine; (b) The tank shall be filled with water to which the hypochlorite solution is added during the filling in sufficient quantity so that the treated water in the tank will contain at least 10 parts per million of available chlorine; (c) The chlorinated water shall be allowed to remain in the tank for two hours; (d) Finally, the tank shall be drained completely before refilling.

Ques: What are the rules as to the tightness of plumbing joints and connections?

Ans: Joints and connections shall be made gas and water tight.

Ques: What type of joints is required in vitrified clay pipes?

Ans: Joints in vitrified clay sewer pipe shall be firmly packed with oakum or hemp and shall be secured with cement, mortar, or asphaltic compound at least 1 inch thick.

Ques: How shall calked joints be made?

Ans: Brass calking ferrules shall be either of the best quality of cast brass or shall be of the cold-drawn seamless tube variety, with weights and dimensions in accordance with Table 1. Soldering nipples shall be of brass pipe (iron-pipe size) or heavy cast brass of at least the weight shown in Table 1. Soldering bushings shall be of brass pipe (iron-pipe size) or heavy brass or copper.

Table 1. Weight of Soldering Nipples

Pipe size (inches)	Actual inside diameter (inches)	Length (inches)	Weight	
			Pounds	Ounces
2.............................	2¼	4½	1	....
3.............................	3¼	4½	1	12
4.............................	4¼	4½	2	8

Ques: What type of screw joints shall be made in a plumbing system?

Ans: Screw joints shall be tapered with the threads sharp and true, and all burrs due to cutting reamed out smooth. Where fitting compounds, red lead, white lead, or other joint materials are used in making up threaded joints, such materials shall be applied to the male threads only.

Ques: What type of wiped solder joints shall be made in a plumbing system?

Ans: Joints in lead pipes, brass or copper pipes, ferrules, soldering nipples, bushings, or traps, shall in all cases be full-wiped joints, either manufactured or made in the field. An exposed surface of the solder at least 3/4 inch, with a minimum thickness at the thickest part of the joint of 3/8 inch should be on each side of the joint. It shall be unlawful to use overcast or cup joints.

Ques: What are the rules for making joints of lead to cast iron, steel, or wrought iron?

Ans: Joints of lead to cast iron, steel, or wrought iron, shall be made by means of a calking ferrule, soldering nipple, or bushing.

Ques: What type of fixture flanges shall be used in a plumbing system?

Ans: Flanges to receive fixture outlets shall be at least 3/16 inch thick and shall be made of brass or bronze. (Some local codes allow the use of plastic pipe).

Ques: What are the rules for connections between drainage pipes and water closets, pedestal urinal and trap, and standard slop sinks in a plumbing system?

271

Ans: The connections between drainage pipes and water closets, floor outlet slop sinks, pedestal urinals and earthenware trap standards, shall be made by means of brass flanges calked to the drainage pipes. Such connections may be wiped or soldered to lead pipes. Such connections shall be bolted to the earthenware with an approved gasket or washer between the earthenware and the connection. Floor outlet connections shall be set on an approved floor slab or ring made of materials impervious to moisture.

Ques: When are slip joints and unions permitted?

Ans: Slip joints or unions shall be permitted only in trap seals or on the inlet side of the trap, except where it is impracticable to otherwise provide for expansion in stacks of unusual height. The authorities may permit the use of an approved type of expansion joint which comprises, in part, a slip joint.

Ques: What are the rules as to roof joint connections in a plumbing system?

Ans: Where the pipes pass through roofs, the joints shall be made watertight by the use of copper, lead, or cast-iron plates or flashings.

Ques: How are expansion and contraction of piping due to temperature variations provided for in a plumbing system?

Ans: In structures over 150 feet high, adequate means shall be provided for taking care of the expansion and contraction of all vertical lines of pipe.

Ques: What are the rules as to welding of joints in a plumbing system?

Ans: Joints and connections for water or gas pipe made of brass, copper, black steel, or black wrought iron, or combinations of these materials, may be made by welding. It shall be unlawful to weld any galvanized pipe, cast-iron pipe, or any drain, soil, or vent pipe of any material.

Ques: What type of sleeves is prohibited on soil or waste lines in a plumbing system?

Ans: It shall be unlawful to use double hubs or sleeves on soil or waste lines. It shall be unlawful to drill or tap house drains, soil, waste, or vent pipes, or to use saddle hubs or bands.

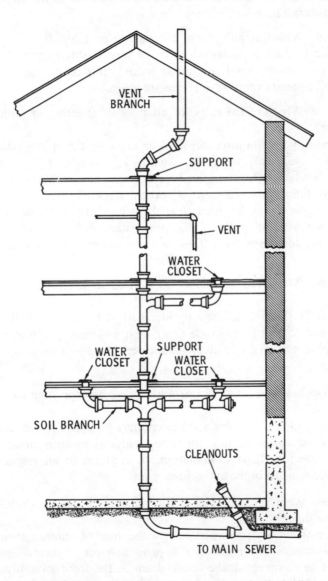

Fig. 4. Showing layout of soil pipe in a typical one-family dwelling.

273

Ques: What is the rule for protection of soil or waste stacks.
Ans: Soil or waste stacks shall be installed inside the structure, as shown in Fig. 4.

Ques: What plumbing connections are prohibited?
Ans: It shall be unlawful to make any waste connection to a bend of a water closet or similar fixture. It shall be unlawful to use soil or waste vents as soil or waste pipes.

Ques: What are the rules for changes in direction in plumbing system?
Ans: Changes in direction shall be made by the appropriate use of 45° wyes, half wyes, long-sweep 1/4 bends, 1/6, 1/8, or 1/16 bends, or long-turn tee-wye fittings, except that short-turn tee-wye fittings may be used on vertical stacks. Fittings other than the foregoing may be used if such fittings are approved in accordance with the rules of the authorities. All 1/4 bends shall be of the long-turn type. Tees and crosses may be used in vent pipes.

Ques: What grade or slope is required in horizontal drainage piping?
Ans: Horizontal drainage piping shall be run in practical alignment and at a uniform grade of at least 1/8 inch per foot for 4-inch pipe and larger, and 1/4 inch per foot for 3-inch pipe and smaller.

Ques: May old house drains and sewers be connected to a new structure?
Ans: Old house drains and sewers may be used for connections to new structures or new plumbing only when such drains and sewers are found, on examination, to conform in all respects to the requirements of the authorities.

Ques: What are the rules for connection of house drains for rear buildings?
Ans: When a structure stands in the rear of another structure on the same interior lot, and a private sewer is unavailable or cannot be constructed, the house drain of the front structure may be extended to the rear, and is considered as one house drain.

Ques: What are the rules as to location of house sewers?

Ans: It shall be unlawful to lay house sewers within 10 feet of any foundation or property line unless such sewers are constructed of cast-iron pipe and approved by local authorities.

Ques: What are the rules as to provision of house traps and fresh-air inlets when installing plumbing fixtures or leaders?

Ans: Every structure in which plumbing fixtures or leaders are installed shall be provided with a house trap. Such traps shall be located on the house drain near the front wall of the structure inside the property line and on the sewer side of all connections, except a connection used to receive the discharge from a sewer lift, oil separator, blow-off pipe, or leaders. If such traps are placed outside of a house or below a cellar floor, such traps shall be made accessible in a masonry manhole with an approved cover.

A fresh-air inlet pipe shall be provided for each house drain discharging directly into a house trap. Such fresh-air inlet pipes shall connect with the house drain just ahead of the house trap, and the inlet pipe shall be of a diameter at least half the diameter of the house drain where the inlet pipe connects, and shall extend to the outer air and terminate in an open end at least 6 inches above grade. Such open ends shall be protected by a perforated metal plate permanently fixed in the mouth of the inlet. Such metal plates shall have a clear ventilating area at least equal to the area of the pipe. It shall be unlawful to use curb boxes or similar devices with gratings placed in sidewalks as fresh-air inlets.

Ques: What are the rules for installation of floor drains?

Ans: Floor drains should have a minimum water seal of 3 inches, and be provided with removable strainers. It is recommended that the open area be at least two-thirds of the cross-sectional area of the drain line to which it is connected. If floor drains are subject to back flow, they must not be connected directly to the drainage system. Size of connection traps shall be such that they can be easily cleaned, and of a size to efficiently serve the intended purpose. The drain inlet shall be located so that it is in full view at all times. When floor drains are subject to back flow or back pressure, they shall be equipped (subject to the approval of the authorities) with adequate back-water valves of a type approved by the board. Shower-bath drains, drains in floor urinals, or any other drain used as part of or in connection with a plumbing fixture, shall be considered a plumbing fixture drain. Floor drains in garages or other structures, where such drains receive the discharge of oils and similar substances, shall be installed as provided by authorities.

Ques: What is meant by the term *fixture unit,* and how was this term derived?

Ans: The unit system has been formulated from tests conducted by the subcommittee on plumbing of the Building Code Committee under the Department of Commerce. Standard plumbing fixtures were installed and individually tested, and the amount of liquid waste which could be discharged through their outlet orifices in a given interval was carefully measured.

During the test it was found that a wash basin, which is one of the smaller plumbing fixtures, would discharge waste in the amount of approximately 7-1/2 gallons of water per minute. Since 1 cubic foot contains 7.4805 gallons, it will be observed that this volume was so close to a cubic foot of water that the committee decided to establish it as a basis of the unit system and termed the discharge of the wash basin as one fixture unit. Therefore, one fixture unit represents approximately 7-1/2 gallons of water.

Table 2. Fixture Unit Values

Fixture	Units
Lavatory or wash basin	1
Kitchen sink	1½
Bathtub	2
Laundry tub	2
Combinaiton fixture	3
Urinal	3
Shower bath	3
Floor drain	2
Slop sink	4
Water closet	6
One bathroom group (consisting of water closet, lavatory, bathtub, and overhead shower, or water closet, lavatory, and shower compartment)	8
180 square feet of roof drained	1

Ques: What are the values in fixture units for common plumbing fixtures?

Ans: Table 2 is based on the rate of discharge from a wash basin or lavatory as the unit employed to determine fixture equivalents.

Ques: What determines the size of waste outlet in fixtures?

Ans: The size of waste outlets in fixtures is determined by the type and number of fixtures installed. Table 3 gives the approximate size of waste outlets for various numbers of fixture units.

Table 3. Waste Sizes for Various Fixture Units

Size of waste outlet in fixtures	Number of units
½ inch, ¾ inch, less than 1 inch	½
1 inch	1
1¼ inches	2
1½ inches	3
2 inches	5½
2½ inches	8
3 inches	15
4 inches	30
5 inches	50
6 inches	80
8 inches	160

Ques: What are the requirements for roof extensions of soil and waste stacks?

Ans: Roof extensions of soil and waste stacks or roof vents shall be run at full size at least 1 foot above any roof pitched at an angle of 30° or more from the horizontal. Such extensions shall be run full size at least 5 feet where the roof is used for any purpose other than weather protection. If the roof terminal of any vent, soil, or waste pipe is within 10 feet of any door, window, scuttle, or airshaft, such roof terminal shall extend at least 3 feet above such opening.

When soil, waste, or vent pipe are extended through the roof, they shall be at least 4 inches in size. Pipes smaller than 4 inches shall be provided with a proper increaser located just below the roof line.

Ques: What are the minimum sizes of individual soil and waste branches?

Ans: Minimum sizes of soil or waste branches to individual fixtures shall be in accordance with the Table 4. The size of any stack, house drain, or house sewer shall be at least that of the largest branch connected to it.

Table 4. Soil and Waste Branch Sizes for Various Fixtures

Fixture	Branch Size
Water closet	3 inches
Floor drains	3 inches
Urinal	2 inches
Slop sink	3 inches
Sink, except slop sink	2 inches
Bathtub	1½ inches
Laundry tray	1½ inches
Shower bath	2 inches
Lavatory	1½ inches
Drinking fountain	1½ inches
Dental cuspidor	1½ inches
Sterilizers with ½-inch waste outlet	1½ inches
Combination fixture, laundry tubs, and kitchen sinks	2 inches

Ques: What determines the size of branch soils and wastes in a plumbing system?

Ans: The required size of branch soils and wastes receiving the discharge of two or more fixtures shall be determined on the basis of the total number of fixture units drained by branch soils and wastes, in accordance with Table 5.

Ques: What are the minimum size waste stacks required for water closets?

Ans: No water closet shall discharge into a stack less than 3 inches in diameter. Not more than one water closet shall be permitted to discharge into a 3-inch stack or branch.

Ques: What are the rules for installation of oil separators?

Ans: When the liquid wastes from any structure consist wholly or in part of volatile, inflammable oil, and an oil separator is re-

Table 5. Size of Piping for Branch and Soil Wastes

Maximum number of fixture units permitted	Maximum number of water closets permitted	Diameter of branch (inches)
2	....	1½
9	....	2
20	....	2½
35	1	3
100	11	4
250	28	5

quired by law, the fixtures receiving such wastes shall be connected to an independent drainage system discharging into such a separator. Every oil separator shall have an individual 3-inch vent extending from the top of such separator to the outer air at a point at least 12 feet above street level. The discharge from the oil separator shall be either independently connected to the sewer or to the sewer side of the house trap. A separator shall be accepted in lieu of a house trap.

A fresh-air inlet shall be provided from the drain at the inlet side of the separator to the outer air, and such inlet shall terminate with the open end at least 6 inches above grade. The diameter of such inlet pipe shall be equal to the diameter of such drain, but in any case, such diameter shall be 3 inches or more. The horizontal drain and one riser shall be at least 3 inches in diameter. Risers shall be carried full size through the roof. Oil separators shall be installed in accordance with rules of the authorities.

Ques: What are the rules as to the discharge of acid in a plumbing system?

Ans: It shall be unlawful to discharge into the regular plumbing system any acids or liquids of any kind which may be injurious to such a system. Such acids or liquids shall be discharged through an independent system directly to the sewer. Piping for both drainage and vents shall be of acid-resisting material approved by the authorities.

The authorities may, however, permit the discharge into the regular plumbing system of chemically neutralized acid waste or other liquids which would otherwise be injurious to the system if,

279

in their opinion, the treatment of these liquids renders them no more harmful than regular waste and drainage.

Ques: May waste from an oil storage plant be connected to a public drain or sewer?

Ans: It shall be unlawful to connect an oil storage plant with any public drain or sewer, or to permit any liquid product of petroleum to escape into any such drain or sewer.

Ques: What are the rules for employing a combined storm and sanitary drainage system in a plumbing system?

Ans: Whenever a combined storm and sanitary drainage system is employed, the required sizes of all parts of such system shall be determined by adding to the drained area an allowance in square feet for each fixture unit on the sanitary system, except that combined sanitary and storm house sewers shall be at least 4 inches in size. Such allowance shall be determined in accordance with the following.

Add to the drained area the following number of square feet:

30 for each of the first	6 fixture units
20 for each of the first	4 fixture units
14 for each of the first	10 fixture units
9 for each of the first	10 fixture units
6 for each of the first	1470 fixture units
5 for each of the first	1500 fixture units
4 for each of the first	2000 fixture units
3 for each fixture unit thereafter.	

The required sizes of the sanitary system and the storm system up to their point of junction may be independently determined from the tables applying to these separate systems. The required sizes of storm-water house drains, house sewers, and all other storm-water piping, shall be determined on the basis of the total drained area in horizontal projection in accordance with Table 6.

The size of the horizontal run from the base of the leader to the house drain, including the trap, shall be in accordance with Table 6. Leaders shall be at least the size required in column C of the table.

Table 6. Size of Piping for Storm Water Only

Diameter of pipe (inches)	Maximum Drained Area in Square Feet		
	A Fall, ⅛ inch per foot	B Fall, ¼ inch per foot	C Fall, ½ inch per foot
2	250	350	500
2½	450	600	900
3	700	1000	1500
4	1500	2100	3000
5	2700	3800	5500
6	4300	6100	9000
8	9600	13,000	19,000
10	16,500	24,000	35,000
12	27,000	40,000	56,000

Ques: How shall drainage of yard areas and roofs be accomplished?

Ans: Yard areas, courts, and court yards (if paved), together with all roofs, shall be drained into a storm sewer or combined sewer. When drains used for such purposes are connected with the combined sewer, such drains shall be effectively trapped. One trap may serve all such connections. All traps shall be protected against frost. It shall be unlawful to drain such yard areas, courts, court yards, and roofs into sewers intended for sewage only.

Ques: What are the rules as to employment of leaders and gutters on buildings?

Ans: Every building shall be provided with gutters and leaders for disposing of water from the roof in such manner as to prevent injury to the walls and foundations, except that the authorities, at their discretion, may grant permission for the omission of gutters and leaders in special cases. When such gutters or leaders are omitted, the surface of the ground adjacent to the foundation walls shall be graded so as to prevent injury to the walls and foundations.

Ques: What method shall be employed for protection of traps in a plumbing system?

Ans: Every fixture trap shall be protected against siphonage and back pressure. Every fixture trap shall be individually vented, except as otherwise provided in this section, and except that the top-most fixture may be without a vent if such a fixture is within 2 feet of the main waste or soil stack. It shall be unlawful to install crown vents.

In schools, traps of sinks in chemical laboratories may be installed without vents, provided that:

1. Traps installed are the deep-seal type.

2. Wastes are connected to an independent stack of acid-resisting materials which serves chemical laboratory fixtures on not more than two floors, and which extends without other connections to an independent house trap and house sewer, except that all similar laboratory stacks may be connected into a single line which is connected through the independent house trap to the street sewer.

Ques: How shall vent pipes be graded?

Ans: Vent and branch vent pipes shall be free from drops or sags, or such pipes shall be graded and connected as to drip back by gravity to a soil or waste pipe. Where vent pipes connect to a horizontal soil or waste pipe, the vent branch shall be taken off above the center line of the pipe, and the vent pipe shall rise vertically or at an angle of 45° to the vertical before offsetting horizontally or connecting to the branch, main waste, or soil vent.

Ques: What is the maximum permissible distance between vent and trap seal?

Ans: The maximum distance from the vent intersection with the waste or soil pipe to the dip of the trap shall be 2 feet developed length. The vent opening from the soil or waste pipe, except for water closets and similar fixtures, shall be above the dip of the trap. Branch vent lines shall be kept above the tops of all connecting fixtures in order to prevent the use of vent pipes as soil or waste pipes.

Ques: What is the required size of the vent?

Ans: The required size of the vent shall be determined on the basis of the size of the soil or waste stack, the number of fixture units connected to the vent, and the developed length of the pipe, in accordance with Table 7. Vents shall be at least 1-1/2 inches in diameter. The diameter of every vent stack shall be at least one-half the diameter of the soil or waste stack served. In determining the developed length of vent pipes, the vent stack and branches shall be considered continuous.

Where main stacks are grouped together at the top of a structure into one pipe which extends through the roof, such combined vent shall be at least equal in area to 75% of the sum of the areas of the stacks connecting into such combined vent.

Ques: Where shall main vents be connected?

Ans: Main vents or vent stacks shall connect at their base to the main soil or waste pipe at least 3 feet below the lowest vent

Table 7. Vent Stacks and Branches

Diameter of pipe (inches)	Maximum number of fixture units permitted	Maximum developed length in feet for each size
1½	6	25
2	40	60
2½	72	100
3	120	150
4	250	250
5	500	300
6	1250	400
8	2400	Unlimited
10	3000	Unlimited
12	5000	Unlimited

branch. The size of such connection shall be as prescribed in the foregoing paragraphs. Such stacks shall extend undiminished and unincreased in size above the roof, or such stacks shall be reconnected with the main soil or waste stacks at least 3 feet above the highest fixture branch. Wherever possible, the base of the vent shall receive the wash of the adjoining soil or waste.

Ques: What are the rules for installation of local vent connections?

Ans: Local vent pipes from fixtures, when installed, shall be entirely distinct from other ventilating ducts, flues, or pipes in the structure. Local vent pipes in which condensation may collect shall be provided with drips. Such drips shall either be connected as an indirect waste or shall be connected to the house side of a fixture trap.

Ques: What are the rules for offsets in soil, waste, and vent stacks?

Ans: When cast-iron bell-and-spigot pipe is used, offsets in soil and waste stacks above the highest fixture connection and offsets in vent stacks and connections of such vent stacks to a soil or waste pipe at the bottom, or to the house drain, shall be made at an angle of at least 45° to the horizontal. Where it is impractical because of structural conditions to provide a 45° angle, the authorities may permit a reduction in the angle under such conditions as they may prescribe, and when it constitutes a vent extension of the vertical waste from the two fixtures. It should be installed with a sanitary cross and not closer than 6 inches to the dip of either trap, each trap to be within 2 feet from the unit vent. This also applies to a horizontal connection if the common vent is taken off at the point of intersection of the fixture branches.

Ques: What are the requirements as to materials in plumbing fixtures?

Ans: Plumbing fixtures shall be made of impervious materials with a smooth surface which shall be easily kept clean. Water-closet bowls and traps shall be made of glazed vitreous earthenware, in one piece, and shall be of such form as to hold a sufficient quantity of water when filled to the trap overflow. To prevent fouling of the surfaces, such bowls and traps shall be provided with integral flushing rims so constructed as to flush the entire interior of the bowl. It shall be unlawful to use rubber connections on flush pipes. Urinals shall be made of glazed earthenware.

Ques: What are the rules as to location of water closets?

Ans: Outside location of water closets is prohibited. Water-closet accommodations shall be placed inside the structures which they serve, except as provided for temporary privies, or privies to be used where no public sewer is available. Whenever a street sewer connection is available, it shall be unlawful to replace an inside water closet with an outside water closet.

Ques: What types of water closets are prohibited?

Ans: It shall be unlawful tc have pans, plungers, offset wash-out and washout, or other water closets having unventilated spaces or walls which are not thoroughly washed out at each flushing. Long hopper closets may be permitted only when the authorities are convinced that there is exposure to frost.

Ques: What are the rules as to flushing and overflow of water closets?

Ans: Every water closet or urinal shall be flushed from a separate flush tank, the water from which is used for that purpose only, or such water closet or urinal shall be flushed through an approved flush valve. It shall be unlawful to connect water closets or urinals directly to a water supply system, except through approved flush valves so located as to prevent pollution of the water supply. Overflows of flush tanks may discharge into water closets or urinals, but it shall be unlawful to connect such overflows with any part of the drainage system.

Ques: What flush pipe sizes are required for use on water closets?

Ans: Water-closet flush pipes shall be at least 1-1/4 inches in diameter, and urinal flush pipes shall be at least 1 inch in diameter. Such pipes may be of copper tubing at least 0.0313 inch in thickness (No. 22 U. S. gauge). Flush pipes shall be of nonferrous metal.

Ques: Are wooden enclosures permitted on plumbing fixtures?

Ans: Fixtures shall be devoid of any permanent wood enclosures.

Ques: What are the rules with regard to the employment of antisiphon devices on plumbing fixtures?

Ans: Wherever the supply to a fixture is introduced into such fixture below the overflow level, such supply shall be provided with an approved vacuum breaker which will prevent the siphoning of water from such fixture into the supply piping.

Ques: What is the required capacity of water-closet flush tanks?

Ans: Each water closet shall be supplied with at least 4 gallons at each flushing, and flush tanks shall be of sufficient capacity to supply the required volume. Each urinal shall be supplied with at least 2 gallons at each flushing, and flush tanks shall be of sufficient capacity to supply the required volume.

Ques: What are the rules for determining the number of toilet fixtures required in a public building?

Ans: Every office building, school, store, warehouse, manufacturing establishment, or other structure where workmen or workwomen are or will be employed, shall be provided with at least one water closet. Water closets shall be provided for each sex according to Table 8. The number of water closets to be provided for each sex shall, in every case, be based upon the maximum number of persons of that sex employed at any one time on the given floor, or in the structure for which such closets are provided.

Table 8. Number of Water Closets Required

Number of persons	Number of closets	Ratio
1- 15	1	1 for 15
16- 35	2	1 for 17½
36- 55	3	1 for 18⅓
56- 80	4	1 for 20
81-110	5	1 for 22
111-150	6	1 for 25
151-190	7	1 for 27½

Ques: What are the requirements as to location of water closets?

Ans: Water closets shall be readily accessible to the persons using them. It shall be unlawful to locate water closets more than one floor above or below the regular working place of the persons using them, except that the authorities may determine the location of water closets in warehouses, garages, and similar structures of low occupancy. The requirement of this section as to location shall be inapplicable when passenger elevators are provided in sufficient numbers, and employees are permitted to use such elevators in going to the toilet-room floors.

Ques: What are the rules as to installation of traps in plumbing fixtures?

Ans: Each fixture shall be separately trapped as near to such fixture as possible, except that a battery of two or three laundry trays, one sink, and two laundry trays or two compartment sinks may connect with a single trap when the outlets of such types of fixtures are 2 inches or less. Traps shall be as near to the fixture as possible, but such traps shall in any case be within 2 feet developed length from the outlet of such fixture. It shall be unlawful to discharge the waste from a bathtub or other fixture into the water-closet trap or bend. It shall be unlawful to double-trap fixtures.

Ques: What is the required design for fixture traps?

Ans: Traps shall be self-cleaning and water-sealed, and shall have a scouring action. Traps for bathtubs, lavatories, sinks, and other similar fixtures shall either be integral or shall be of lead, brass, cast iron, or galvanized malleable iron. Traps shall have a full-size bore and a smooth interior waterway such that a solid ball, 1/4-inch smaller in diameter than the specified diameter of the trap, will pass freely from the outlet end entirely through the seal of the trap. The minimum diameter given is for the soil or waste branch, except that in the case of water-closets, the required minimum shall be 2-1/2 inches. In cases other than fixtures, the size of the trap shall be the same as the size of the discharge pipe connecting thereto.

Ques: What is the minimum water seal of a fixture trap?

Ans: Fixture traps shall have a water seal of at least 2 inches. All other traps shall have a water seal of at least 3 inches. This is illustrated in Fig. 5.

Ques: What are the rules as to setting and protection of fixture traps?

Ans: Traps shall be set true with respect to their water seals and shall be protected from frost and evaporation.

Ques: What is the required construction for back-water valves?

Ans: Back-water valves shall have all bearing parts made of corrosion-resisting metal, and such valves shall be so constructed as to ensure a positive mechanical seal and remain closed, except when discharging wastes. Back-water valves shall be the approved type.

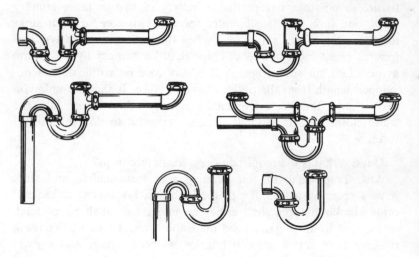

Fig. 5. Showing typical fixture traps.

Ques: What type of fixture traps is prohibited in a plumbing system?

Ans: Full "S" traps are prohibited as well as bell traps. Traps having covers, hand holes, or clean-outs held in place by lugs or bolts acting as interceptors for grease, or similar substances, may be used if such traps are approved by the board.

Ques: What type of clean-outs is required in fixture traps?

Ans: Easily accessible clean-outs shall be provided at the foot of each vertical waste, soil stock, or inside leader, on all hand holes of running traps, on all exposed or accessible fixture traps (except earthenware traps), and at each change of direction of horizontal runs. Clean-outs shall be of the same nominal size as the pipes up to 4 inches, and such clean-outs shall be at least

4 inches for larger pipes. The maximum distance between the clean-outs in horizontal soil lines shall be 50 feet. A typical sewer clean-out is illustrated in Fig. 6.

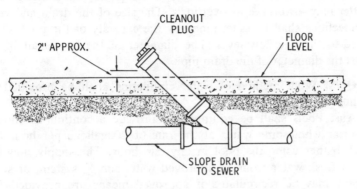

Fig. 6. Illustrating a typical clean-out in a soil-pipe sewer.

Ques: What is considered as a clean-out equivalent in a plumbing system?

Ans: If a fixture trap or a fixture with a trap that is integral can be easily removed without damaging or disturbing the roughing-in work that is concealed, the device can be designated as a clean-out equivalent. But only if there is not more than a single 90° bend in the line which is subject to be rodded. In a single-story building where sink or lavatory traps are easily removed and are accessible, these traps may be considered as clean-out equivalents.

Ques: How shall swimming pools be constructed?

Ans: Pools shall be built watertight. The inside surface shall be made of a smooth, nonabsorbent material with rounded corner, and shall be so constructed as to be easily cleaned.

Ques: How shall swimming pools be drained?

Ans: Pools shall be provided with a drain outlet located so that the entire pool can be emptied. Pools shall also be supplied with an overflow at the high-water line. Such drains shall be at least 3 inches in diameter and shall be trapped before connecting with the drainage system. The trap shall be vented. Such overflow shall be connected to the inlet side of the trap and on the sewer side of the valve on the emptying drain. Drain and circulating outlets shall be fitted with a device to reduce the vortex. The spaces around the pool shall be drained in such a manner as to prevent the water from draining into the pool. The drains in the gutter may also serve as overflows. The size of the drain and vent connections shall be determined by the capacity of the pool when filled to the overflow level. The diameter of the trap shall be at least the diameter of the drain pipe.

Ques: What method of water circulation shall be provided in swimming pools?

Ans: Pools shall be equipped to provide a continuous supply of clear wholesome water at the rate of 20 gallons per hour for each bather using the pool in any one hour. The supply may be either fresh water from an approved water supply system, or such supply may be recirculated if approved means are provided for filtering and sterilizing the water before such water is reintroduced into the pool. The inlets shall be located so as to circulate the water over the entire area of the pool.

The piping of the recirculating system shall be kept entirely separate from the city or domestic supply system. Sterilizing and filtration equipment shall be adequate to keep the pool in a sanitary condition at all times. Adequate shower-bath and toilet accommodations, conveniently located for the use of the bathers, shall be provided for all pools.

Ques: Shall swimming pools be provided with sterilization and filtration equipment?

Ans: Yes. Sterilizing and filtration equipment shall be adequate to keep the pool in a sanitary condition at all times.

Ques: What are the rules as to provisions for shower bath and toilet facilities in connection with the operation of swimming pools?

Ans: Adequate shower-bath and toilet accommodations, conveniently located for the use of the bathers, shall be provided for all pools.

CHAPTER 10

General Plumbing Information

The ability to perform elementary calculations is a prime necessity, not only for the plumber's license aspirant, but for the practicing master plumber as well. With this in view, a number of practical examples, or problems bearing on the subject matter, have been calculated. Although requirements for plumber's licenses may differ somewhat in various localities, the problems giving are of a type usually found in license examinations for master plumbers. In this connection, it should be impressed upon all candidates for licenses the great necessity of careful study to master the fundamental principles underlying each example given in order to perfect themselves so as to be able to solve any new or similar problem at the written examination.

Example—A water tank is 65 inches long and has a trapezoidal cross-section. The two parallel sides are 32 inches and 44 inches and the distance between them is 40 inches. Determine the capacity of the tank in gallons.

Solution—The formula for calculating the area of a trapezoid is:

$$A = \frac{1}{2} H (a + b)$$

where

H is the distance between the two parallel sides
a and b is the length of the parallel sides
A is the area

A substitution of numerical values gives:

$$A = \frac{1}{2} \times 40 \ (32 + 44) = 1520 \text{ sq. in.}$$

The volume in cubic inches $= 1520 \times 65 = 98,800$

Since there are 231 cubic inches in one gallon, the gallon contents of the tank $=$

$$\frac{98,800}{231} = 427.7 \text{ gals.}$$

Example—What is the radius of a circle the area of which is equal to that of a rectangle whose sides are 26.9 and 12.5 in. respectively?

Solution — Area of rectangle $= 26.9 \times 12.5 = 336.25$ sq. in.

Area of circle $= \pi R^2 = 336.25$ sq. in.

From which $R = \dfrac{\sqrt{336.25}}{\pi} = 10.34$ in.

Example — What is the weight of a solid ball of brass 6 inches in diameter? Assume specific gravity $= 8.4$

Solution — The cubic contents of the ball is obtained by the use of the following formula:

$$V = \frac{4\pi R^3}{3} = \frac{4\pi \times 3^3}{3} = 113.1 \text{ cu. in.}$$

Weight of the ball equals the weight of one cubic inch of water $\times$ specific gravity of brass $\times$ circumference of the ball. Therefore:

Weight of ball = 0.0361 × 8.4 × 113.1 = 34.3 lbs.

Example — Find the height of a cast-iron cone whose weight is 533.4 kilogram, and whose diameter at the base is 5 decimeters. (Specific gravity of cast iron = 7.22)

Solution — The cubic content of the cone is:

$$\frac{533.4}{7.22} = 73.9 \text{ cubic decimeters}$$

$$\text{Volume of cone} = \frac{\text{base area} \times H}{3}$$

It follows that

$$73.9 = \frac{5 \times 5 \times 0.7854 \times H}{3}$$

and

$$H = \frac{3 \times 73.9}{5 \times 5 \times 0.7854}$$
$$= 11.3 \text{ decimeters, or } 11.3 \times 3.937$$
$$= 44.5 \text{ inches (approx.)}$$

Example — In a certain plumbing installation, three pipes have an internal diameter of 2, 2-1/2, and 3 inches, respectively. What is the diameter of a pipe having an area equal to the three pipes?

Solution — The areas of the three pipes are as follows:

$$A_1 + A_2 + A_3 = \frac{\pi \times 2^2}{4} + \frac{\pi \times 2.5^2}{4} + \frac{\pi \times 3^2}{4} =$$

$$\frac{\pi}{4}(2^2 + 2.5^2 + 3^2) = \frac{\pi}{4}(4 + 6.25 + 9) = \frac{\pi}{4} \times 19.25 \text{ sq. in.}$$

Since the formula for a circular area is $\frac{\pi \times D^2}{4}$, we obtain

293

$$\frac{\pi}{4} \times 19.25 = \frac{\pi}{4} \times D^2, \text{ or } D^2 = 19.25 \text{ sq. ins.}$$

Therefore,

$$D = \sqrt{19.25}, \text{ or } 4.39 \text{ inches.}$$

Remember that the area of any circular pipe is directly proportional to the square of its diameter in inches, so our calculation will be somewhat simplified. We have:

$$2^2 + 2.5^2 + 3^2 = D^2$$

or,

$$D = \sqrt{19.25} = 4.39 \text{ inches}$$

It follows from the foregoing that the area of a pipe having the same capacity as a 2, 2-1/2, and 3-inch diameter pipe together, must be 4.39 inches in diameter, or 4-25/64 inches.

Example—If a 1-inch pipe delivers 10 gallons of water per minute, what size of a pipe will be required to deliver 20-gallons per minute?

Solution—In this problem, it is necessary to find the diameter of a piece of pipe whose area is twice as large as one which is 1 inch in diameter. Since the area for any circular section $= \frac{\pi D^2}{4}$, it follows that the area for the 1-inch pipe is $\frac{\pi \times 1^2}{4} = 0.7854$ sq. in. A pipe having twice this area consequently has a diameter of $\frac{\pi}{2}$. Thus, $\frac{\pi}{2} = \frac{\pi D^2}{4}$, which after rearrangement of terms gives $D^2 = 2$, or $D = \sqrt{2} = 1.4142$ inches. That is, the required diameter of a pipe to deliver 20 gpm is 1-13/32 inches (approximately).

Example—If the total fall of a house sewer is 24 inches per 120 feet, what is the slope per foot of this sewer?

Solution—Since the sewer has a total length of 120 feet, the slope per foot is 24/120, or 0.2 inch.

Example—What is the weight of 1 cubic inch of water if it is assumed that 1 cubic foot weighs 62.5 pounds?

Solution—1 cubic foot contains 12 × 12 × 12, or 1728 cubic inches. Therefore, 1 cubic inch weighs 62.5/1728, or 0.0361 lb. This figure is given in most handbooks and is frequently used to calculate water pressure in tanks, pipes, etc.

Example—What is the weight of a column of water 12 inches high and 1 inch in diameter?

Solution—Since 1 cubic inch of water weighs 0.0361 lb., a column of water 12 inches high weighs 12 × 0.0361, or 0.4332 lb.

Example—What is the pressure in pounds per square inch at the base of a 10-foot water cylinder?

Solution—The pressure may be found by remembering that the 10-foot water column weighs 10 × 12 × 0.0361, or 4.332 psi.

Example—Calculate the minimum water pressure at the city water main, in pounds per square inch, necessary to fill a house tank located on top of a 6-story building when the inlet to the water tank is located at an elevation of 110 feet above the city water main.

Solution—Since 1 cubic inch of water weighs 0.0361 lb., the minimum pressure required is 12 × 110 × 0.0361, or 47.7 psi.

Example—A water tank 10 feet high and 15 feet across is to be constructed of wood. When filled to the bottom of the overflow pipe, its capacity is 11,000 gallons. How high above the inside bottom of the tank should the bottom of the overflow pipe be in order to have the required water capacity in the tank? (One cubic foot equals 7.48 gallons).

Solution—The area of the tank in square feet multiplied by the assumed height of the water in the tank in feet equals the cubic content of the water in cubic feet. Since 1 cubic foot equals 7.48

gallons, the cubic content occupied by the water is 11,000/7.48, or 1470.6 cubic feet.

The equation required for our calculation will therefore be as follows:

$$7.5^2 \times \pi \times H = 1470.6$$

$$H = \frac{1470.6}{56.25\pi} = 8.32 \text{ feet}$$

Thus, the bottom of the overflow pipe should be located 8.32 ft. or 8 feet, 3-27/32 inches above the bottom of the tank.

Example—What is the number of horsepower required to raise 40,000 pounds 200 feet in 5 minutes? Neglect losses.

Solution—By definition, 1 horsepower is equivalent to doing work at a rate of 33,000 lbs. per minute. Thus, in the present problem

$$HP = \frac{\text{foot-pounds}}{33,000 \times t}$$

where

HP is the horsepower required

t is the time in minutes

Substituting values, we obtain

$$HP = \frac{\text{foot-pounds}}{33,000 \times t} = \frac{40,000 \times 200}{33,000 \times 5} = 48.5 \text{ HP}$$

Example—What is the number of horsepower required to lift 10,000 gallons of water per hour to a height of 90 feet. Neglect losses. (Assume weight of water to be 8-1/3 lbs. per gallon.)

Solution:

$$HP = \frac{\text{foot-pounds}}{33,000 \times t} = \frac{10,000 \times 8\text{-}1/3 \times 90}{33,000 \times 60} = 3.79 \text{ HP}$$

Example—A city of 25,000 uses 15 gallons of water per day per capita. If it is required to raise this water 150 ft., what is the number of horsepower required? Neglect losses.

Solution:

$$HP = \frac{\text{foot-pounds}}{33,000 \times t}$$

$$= \frac{15 \times 8\text{-}1/3 \times 25,000 \times 150}{33,000 \times 60 \times 24} = 10 \text{ HP (approx.)}$$

Example—How many gallons of water can a 75-HP engine raise 150 ft. high in 5 hours? One gallon of water weighs 8-1/3 lbs. Neglect losses.

Solution—If the given data is substituted in our formula for horsepower, we obtain:

$$75 = \frac{150 \times 8\text{-}1/3 \times G}{33,000 \times 5 \times 60}$$

$$G = \frac{75 \times 33,000 \times 5 \times 60}{150 \times 8\text{-}1/3} = 594,000 \text{ gallons}$$

Example—A circular tank 20 feet deep and 20 feet in diameter is filled with water. If the average height to which the water is to be lifted is 50 ft., what must be the horsepower of an engine capable of pumping the water out in 2 hours? Neglect losses.

Solution—In this example, it is first necessary to calculate the cubic content of the tank; that is, the cross-sectional area multiplied by its height. Thus,

volume in cu. ft. $= \pi R^2 H = \pi \times 10^2 \times 20 = 6283$ cu. ft.

Since 1 cubic foot of water weighs 62.5 lbs., the total weight of the tank's contents is:

$62.5 \times 6283 = 392,700$ pounds (approx.)

297

Again, using our formula, we have:

$$HP = \frac{\text{foot-pounds}}{33,000 \times t} = \frac{392,700 \times 50}{33,000 \times 2 \times 60} = 5 \text{ HP (approx.)}$$

Example—The suction lift on a pump is 10 ft. and the head pumped against is 100 ft. If the loss due to friction in the pipe line is assumed as 9 ft., and the pump delivers 100 gallons per minute, what is the horsepower delivered by the pump?

Solution—When the water delivered is expressed in gallons per minute (gpm) the formula for horsepower is:

$$HP = \frac{\text{gpm} \times \text{head in feet} \times 8.33}{33,000}$$

A substitution of values gives

$$HP = \frac{100 \times 119 \times 8.33}{33,000} = 3 \text{ HP}$$

Example—A tank having a capacity of 10,000 gallons must be emptied in 2 hours. What capacity pump is required?

Solution—The capacity of the pump in gallons per minute (usually written gpm) is arrived at by dividing the total gallonage of the tank by the time in minutes. Thus,

$$\text{gpm} = \frac{10,000}{2 \times 60} = 83.3 \text{ gpm}$$

Example—What is the net capacity of a double-acting pump having a piston diameter of 3-inches and a stroke of 5-inches when it makes 75 strokes per minute? Assume slip of pump = 5%.

Solution—The rule for obtaining pump capacity is as follows: *Multiply the area of the piston in square inches by the length of the stroke in inches, and by the number of delivery strokes per minute; divide the product by 231 to obtain the theoretical capacity in U.S. gallons.*

298

This rule is most commonly stated in a formula as follows:

$$\text{gpm} = \frac{D^2 \times 0.7854 \times L \times N}{231}$$

where,

gpm = number of gallons pumped per minute
D = diameter of plunger or piston in inches
L = length of stroke in inches
N = number of delivery strokes per minute

A substitution of values in the above formula gives:

$$\text{gpm} = \frac{3^2 \times 0.7854 \times 5 \times 75}{231} = 11.5$$

With a slip of 5%, the total net capacity of the pump is finally $11.5 \times 0.95 = 10.9$ gallons per minute.

Example—What is the hourly net capacity of a 2 × 8 double-acting power pump running at 150 rpm and having a slip of 10%?

Solution—The formula for pump capacity is:

$$\text{gpm} = \frac{D^2 \times 0.7854 \times L \times N}{231}$$

$$= \frac{2^2 \times 0.7854 \times 8 \times 300}{231} = 32.7 \text{ gpm}$$

The hourly net capacity $= 32.7 \times 60 \times 0.9 = 1765.8$ gallons.

It should be observed that if N is taken to represent the number of revolutions of a single double-acting pump, the result is to be multiplied by 2, and if N represents the number of revolutions of a duplex pump, which would be the same as two single pumps, the result must be multiplied by 4.

Example—What is the capacity of a double-acting pump in gallons per minute if the cylinder is 9-inches in diameter, and the stroke 10 inches, when it makes 60 strokes per minute? (Neglect slippage.)

Solution—The capacity of the pump in gallons per minute is

$$gpm = \frac{D^2 \times 0.8754 \times L \times N}{231}$$

$$= \frac{9^2 \times 0.7854 \times 10 \times 60}{231}$$

$$= 165.2 \text{ gpm}$$

Example—A gas engine has a 4-inch piston and the effective pressure acting upon it is 50 lbs. per sq. in. What is the total load on the piston?

Solution—In this example, it is first necessary to determine the total net area of the piston. In multiplying this area by the pressure, we obtain the total load acting upon the piston. Thus,

$$A = \frac{\pi \times 4^2}{4} = 12.57 \text{ sq. in.}$$

Total load = 12.57 × 50 = 628.5 lbs.

Example—What is the indicated horsepower of a 4-cylinder 5 × 6 engine running at 500 rpm and 50 lbs. per sq. in. effective pressure?

Solution—The well-known formula for calculation of indicated horsepower is:

$$IHP = \frac{PLAN}{33,000} \times K$$

where co-efficient (K) = 2 (four-cylinder engine). Substituting our values, we obtain:

$$IHP = \frac{50 \times 6/12 \times 0.7854 \times 5^2 \times 500}{33,000} \times 2 = 14.87$$

Example—The temperature of a furnace as registered by a pyrometer is 2750°F. What is the corresponding reading in Centigrade degrees?

Solution—The equation is:

$$C = 5/9 \ (F - 32)$$
$$C = 5/9 \ (2750 - 32) = 1510°$$

Example—A pail contains 58 lbs. of water having a temperature of 40°F. If heat is applied until the temperature of the water reaches 95°F, what is the amount of Btu supplied to the water?

Solution—The rise in temperature has been 95 − 40 = 55°F. Since one Btu is one pound raised one degree, it follows that to raise 58 pounds 55 degrees requires:

$$58 \times 55 = 3190 \text{ Btu}$$

Example—How many heat units (Btu) are required to raise one pound of water from 55° to 212°F? How many units of work does this represent?

Solution—The number of heat units required is 1 (212 − 55) = 157 Btu

Since the mechanical equivalent of heat is 778, it is only necessary to multiply the number of heat units by this constant to obtain the equivalent number of work units. Thus,

$$157 \times 778 = 122,146 \text{ foot-pounds}$$

Example—In a certain pump installation, it was found that a 2-inch pipe, due to corrosion, had an effective diameter of only 1-1/2 inch. Calculate the loss in cross-sectional area due to corrosion.

Solution—It may easily be shown that the area of any circular pipe varies as the square of its diameter. The loss in cross-sectional area is therefore:

$$(2 \times 2) - (1.5 \times 1.5) = 4 - 2.25, \text{ or } 1.75$$

$$1.75 \times 0.7854 = 1.37 \text{ sq. in. loss}$$

301

Example—It is required to calculate the pipe size for a shallow-well suction pump having a capacity of 300 gallons per hour (see Fig. 1). The horizontal distance between the pump and the well is 75 feet, and the vertical lift is 20 feet plus the 5 feet below water level, as shown in the illustration.

Solution—Bearing in mind that 22 feet is considered the maximum practical suction lift for a shallow-well pump, our calculation will be as follows:

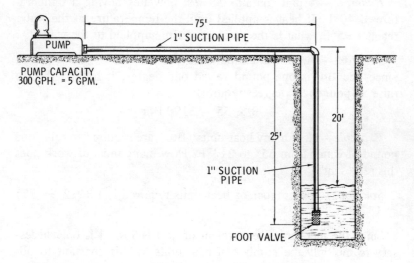

Fig. 1. Illustrating a pipe arrangement for a shallow-well suction pump.

Total water lift	= 20 feet
Total pipe friction loss assuming 5-gpm flow through a 1-inch pipe.	
Vertical part of pipe	= 25 feet
Horizontal part of pipe	= 75 feet
1-inch 90° elbow	= 6 feet
Total footage	=106 feet

As noted in Table 8, the friction loss in a 1-inch pipe at 5 gallons per minute flow equals 3.25 feet per 100 feet of pipe. Since there are 106 feet, the total friction loss = 106/100 × 3.25

= 1.06 × 3.25 = 3.4 feet. The total lift is 20 + 3.4, or 23.4 feet. As noted from our figures, a total lift of 23.4 feet exceeds 22 feet by a considerable margin, and although it is possible that an installation such as the foregoing will work, it should not be attempted as a practical solution.

If, on the other hand, a 1-1/4 in. pipe is selected, a similar reference to our friction-loss table indicates that the friction loss is reduced to 0.84 feet, making a total suction lift of 1.06 × 0.84 + 20 = 20.9 feet, which is within the practical suction limit.

Example—It is necessary to install a shallow-well basement pumping system (see Fig. 2). The horizontal distance between

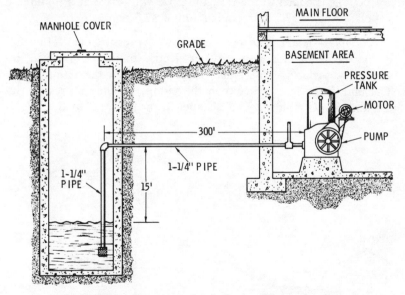

Fig. 2. Piping arrangement of a shallow-well basement pump.

pump and well is 300 feet and the vertical lift is 15 feet. Determine the pipe size and pressure-switch setting for a 5-gpm pump.

Solution—With reference to our friction loss (Table 8), it will be noted that, if a 1-inch pipe is selected, a 5-gpm flow will cause a friction loss of 3.25 feet per 100 feet. Since the total pipe length equals 321 feet (which figure includes the friction loss through the foot valve and elbow), we obtain a total friction loss of 3.25

$\times$ 3.21, or 10.43 feet. The total suction lift is therefore 15 + 10.43, or 25.43 ft. If, on the other hand, a 1-1/4 inch pipe is selected, a similar reference to the friction loss table will give a total loss of 0.84 $\times$ 3.21, or 2.7 ft. The total suction lift using the larger pipe will be 15 + 2.7, or 17.7 feet, which is the size that should be used for this particular installation.

In order to calculate the necessary pressure to overcome the 15-feet elevation and pipe friction loss, the total suction lift value of 17.7 must be multiplied by 62.5/144 or 0.434; that is 17.7 $\times$ 0.434 equals 7.7 pounds pressure. Pressure switches are usually set at 20 pounds minimum and 40 pounds maximum pressure. If 7.7 pounds is added to the foregoing, we will arrive at a minimum switch setting of 27.7 and a maximum of 47.7 pounds.

Example—Water is to be pumped to a pressure tank (Fig. 3) in the basement of a home by an electric motor from a well in which the surface of the water is 85 feet below the pump head. The tank is 15 feet higher than the pump. Maximum pressure in the tank is 40 pounds. The distance from the well to the house

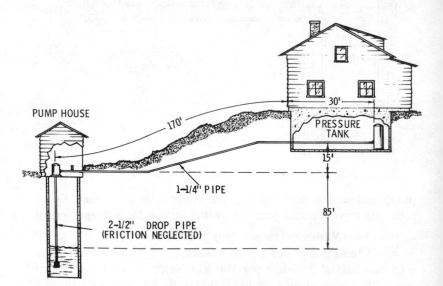

Fig. 3. Piping arrangement of a deep-well pumping system.

is 170 feet, and 30 feet of pipe is required in the house to reach the pressure tank. A 2-1/2 inch drop pipe is being used between the well and the pump, and a 1-1/4 inch pipe from pump to tank. If it is assumed that a 480-gallon per hour pump is used in the installation, what size motor will be required?

Solution—In order to establish the motor size, it will first be necessary to calculate the total head of the pump installation. From the foregoing data we obtain:

Head due to difference in elevation = $\quad 2 \times 2.03 = \quad$ 4.06 ft.
Head due to pressure at tank $\qquad 85 + 15 =$ 100.00 ft.
Total pipe friction loss for the 200
    feet of 1-1/4 inch pipe, assum-
    ing 8 gpm flow (from table) $\quad = 40 \times 2.31 = \quad$ 92.40 ft.
$\qquad\qquad$ Total head $\qquad\qquad\qquad = \overline{\text{196.46 ft.}}$
$\qquad\qquad\qquad\qquad\qquad$ (200 feet approx.)

The theoretical horsepower required may be determined by multiplying the gallons per minute by the total head in feet and dividing the product by 33,000. Since the pump efficiency is not known, we may assume an arbitrary value for our deep-well pump as 30%.

The actual horsepower, therefore $= \dfrac{8 \times 8.34 \times 200}{33,000 \times 0.3} = $ 1-1/3.

Use the next larger standard-size electric motor, which is 1-1/2 horsepower.

Example—A double-acting, single-piston pump has a 2-1/2 inch diameter cylinder and a 3-inch stroke. What is the capacity per revolution?

Solution—In a problem of this type, it will first be necessary to calculate the piston area, which is $2.5^2 \times 0.7854$, or 4.909 square inches. The pump capacity per stroke for one single-acting cylinder in gallons is obviously $4.91 \times 3/231$, or 0.064. Since there is one forward-and-back stroke per revolution in a double-acting pump, the pump capacity per revolution is 0.064×2, or 0.128 gallon.

EFFECT OF PIPE FRICTION LOSS

The friction loss in piping is a very important factor, and must be taken into account when evaluating a water distribution system. The friction loss shown in Table 1 is based on a section of 15-year-old pipe. With reference to this table, it easy to determine the fraction loss through any one of the pipe sizes shown for any flow of water. Thus, for example, a check in our friction-loss table indicates that discharge rate of 5 gallons per minute through 100 feet of 1-inch iron pipe results in a friction loss of 3.25 feet. The same gpm through 100 feet of 3/4-inch pipe will result in a friction loss of 10.5 feet. From the foregoing, it will be noted that pipe friction must be taken into consideration when pipe is selected for the suction line on a shallow-well pump, or for the discharge pipe from the pressure tank to the point of delivery.

Table 1. Friction Loss in Pipe

Flow Gals. per Min.	½ inch		¾ inch		1 inch		1¼ inch		1½ inch		2 inch	
	Ft.	Lbs.	Ft.	Lbs	Ft.	Lbs.	Ft.	Lbs.	Ft.	Lbs	Ft.	Lbs
2	7.4	3.2	1.9	.82								
3	15.8	6.85	4.1	1.78	1.26	.55						
4	27.0	11.7	7.0	3.04	2.14	.93	.57	.25	.26	.11		
5	41.0	17.8	10.5	4.56	3.25	1.41	.84	.36	.40	.17		
6			14.7	6.36	4.55	1.97	1.20	.52	.56	.24	.20	.086
8			25.0	10.8	7.8	3.38	2.03	.88	.95	.41	.33	.143
10			38.0	16.4	11.7	5.07	3.05	1.32	1.43	.62	.50	.216
12					16.4	7.10	4.3	1.86	2.01	.87	.70	.303
14					22.0	9.52	5.7	2.46	2.68	1.16	.94	.406
16					28.0	12.10	7.3	3.16	3.41	1.47	1.20	.520
18							9.1	3.94	4.24	1.83	1.49	.645

PUMP CHARACTERISTICS

Automatic and semiautomatic pump installations for water supply purposes are commonly employing three or four types of pumps. Actually, there are only three types, and while each type has its individual characteristics, they all conform to the same general principles. There is the *reciprocating or plunger type,* the *rotary,* and the *centrifugal;* while the *jet* or *ejector* pump has

306

derived its name from the introduction of a jet system attached to the centrifugal or reciprocating type of pump. A brief tabulation of the characteristics of the various types of pumps are given in Table 2. For convenience, they are listed as to speed, suction lift, and practical pressure head.

Table 2. Pump Characteristics

Type Pump	Speed	Practical Suction Lift	Pressure Head	Delivery Characteristics
Reciprocating: Shallow Well (low pressure) (medium pressure)	Slow 250 to 550 strokes per min.	22 to 25 ft.	40 to 43 lbs. Up to 100 lbs.	Pulsating (air chamber evens pulsations) ''
(high pressure)			Up to 350 lbs.	''
Deep Well	Slow 30 to 52 strokes per min.	Available for lifts up to 875 ft. Suction lift below cylinder 22 ft.	Normal 40 lbs.	''
Rotary Pump: (shallow well)	400 to 1725 rpm	22 ft.	About 100 lbs.	Positive (slightly pulsating)
Ejector Pump: (shallow well and limited deep wells)	Used with centrifugal-turbine or shallow well reciprocating pump.	Max. around 120 ft. Practical at lifts of 80 ft. or less	40 lbs. (normal) Available at up to 70 lbs. pressure head	Continuous nonpulsating, high capacity with low-pressure head
Centrifugal: Shallow Well (single stage)	High, 1750 and 3600 rpm	15 ft. maximum	40 lbs. (normal) 70 lbs. (maximum)	Continuous nonpulsating, high capacity with low-pressure head
Turbine Type: (single impeller)	High, 1750 rpm	28 ft. maximum at sea level	40 lbs. (normal) Available up to 100 lbs. pressure head	Continuous nonpulsating, high capacity with low-pressure head

In the selection of pumps, it cannot be too strongly emphasized that since each pump application will differ, not only in capacity requirement but also in the pressure against which the pump will have to operate, plus other factors, the home owner should consult with the pump manufacturer as to the type of pump which will be best suited for a particular installation.

For example: If a 1/2-inch hose with nozzle is to be used for sprinkling, water will be consumed at the rate of 200 gallons per hour. To permit use of water for other purposes at the same time, it is therefore essential to have a pump capacity in excess of 200 gallons per hour. Where 1/2-inch hose with nozzle is to be used,

307

we recommend the use of a pump having a capacity of at least 220 gallons per hour, which leaves available for other uses water at the rate of 20 gallons per hour when the hose is being used. In determining the desired pump capacity, even for ordinary requirements, it is advisable to select a size large enough so that the pump will not run more than a few hours per day at the most.

Reciprocating pumps will deliver water in quantities proportional to the number of strokes and the length and size of the cylinder. They are adapted to a wide range of speeds, and to practically any depth of well. Since reciprocating pumps are positive in operation, they should be fitted with automatic relief valves to prevent rupture of pipes or other damage should power be applied against abnormal pressure.

If it is not practical to set the pump directly over the well, as is necessary with deep-well plunger pumps, an ejector-type pump may be selected. The ejector pump is most efficient where the lift is between 25 and 65 feet, but will operate with lifts of up to 120 feet. The ejector pump, however, is not usually recommended for wells with depth in excess of 80 feet.

Centrifugal pumps are somewhat critical as to speed and should be used only where power can be applied at a reasonable constant speed. Vertical-type centrifugal pumps are used in deep wells. They are usually driven through shafting by vertical motors mounted at the top of the well. Rather large wells are required for either centrifugal or turbine deep-well pumps, the size depending on the capacity and design of the pump. Centrifugal pumps are efficient in higher capacities, but in the lower capacities of 10 gallons or less per minute, their efficiency is not as high as that of the plunger pumps. It is usually not practical to adopt centrifugal pumps for installations requiring small volumes of water.

Turbine pumps as used in domestic water systems are self-priming. Their smooth operation makes them suitable for applications where noise and vibration must be kept at a minimum.

Ejector pumps are becoming very popular. They operate quietly, and neither the deep-well nor the shallow-well type need to be mounted over the well.

Index